D1283082

The Bears of Big Stream Valley

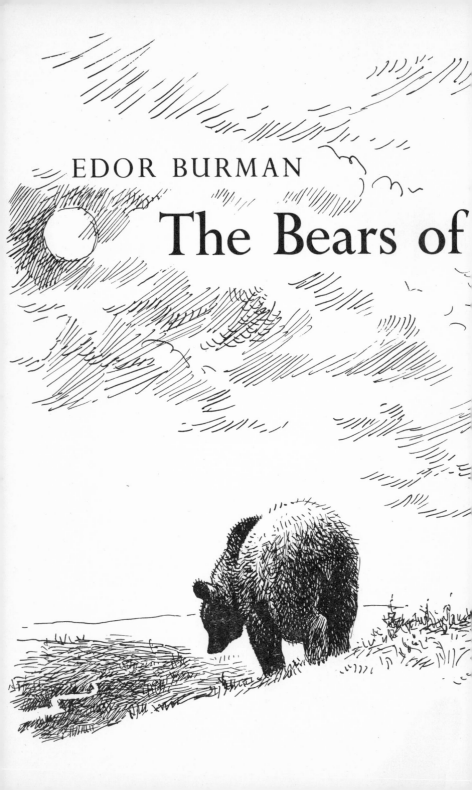

EDOR BURMAN

The Bears of

Big Stream Valley

ILLUSTRATED BY
Harald Wiberg

TRANSLATED FROM THE SWEDISH BY
Gerry Bothmer

A SEYMOUR LAWRENCE BOOK
DELACORTE PRESS

Originally published in Sweden by AB Rabén
& Sjögren Bokförlåg under the title
BJÖRNARNA I STORÅDALEN

© 1965 by Edor Burman
Copyright © 1968 by Dell Publishing Co., Inc.

Manufactured in the United States of America
Library of Congress Catalog Card No.: 68–14981
First printing—1968

Contents

To the Reader

RAMTI is an ordinary brown bear. I have given him a name to make it easier to follow him through forests, valleys, and mountains. He is young and full of curiosity and so he encounters, or seeks out, many adventures in the wilderness. When he is foraging for food, he isn't always as mild-mannered as a story-book teddy bear. On the contrary, he and his comrades deal cruelly with other animals. But he rarely represents a danger to human beings. If they don't flee from him, he will most likely run away himself.

During my travels through the forest I have seen with my own eyes most of the experiences Ramti goes through. The fifty-odd bears I have met have all resembled Ramti in some way. In my story about him I have also included some anecdotes which have been related by other wanderers through the forest.

THE AUTHOR

The Bears of Big Stream Valley

1. The Lair

Ramti was born in a deep hole that his mother had dug into a steep mountain slope. Above the lair was a zigzag of trees, and far below, the jagged banks of Big Stream.

The day was bitterly cold. A faint cloud of steam arose from the lair, which lay under three feet of snow. The warm vapors soon turned to ice on the bent, gnarled mountain birches. A gray fog floated across the sun and suddenly threw everything into gloom and darkness. Down in the valley the ice crackled and snapped as if it were heralding the birth of a new native son of the forest—Ramti, the brown bear.

Akka had been expecting this event for a long time. Throughout the fall she had been busy digging her lair high up on Big Stream Mountain because she wanted to have peace and quiet during the winter months. While the ground was frozen and her footprints left no traces, she had gathered together enough moss for a bed. She was keenly aware of hunters and knew that she had to be on her guard. After having kept watch at the entrance to her cave for almost a week, she had finally crawled in, sighed contentedly and gone off to sleep.

Since then she had slept practically the whole time, for she felt tired and heavy. She had stirred only once, and that was when a hunter, unaware of her presence, had shot at a wolverine close to her lair. For a while she had trembled with anger and terror, but then she had rolled over and fallen asleep again. Like all bears during the winter months, she hibernated; reality was far away.

Today, however, she was wide awake. She listened with growing anxiety to the distant sounds of the axe. They were familiar sounds to her. Last winter and earlier this year, she had heard the same sound day after day. She knew that behind the noise there was a human being, and she had mixed feelings about human beings. But never had she had such a dread of human closeness as today.

With her blunt snout, she gently pushed Ramti to her teats, where he promptly settled down. Sucking loudly, the cub was having his first taste of milk. Fur- less and blind, he soon fell asleep, happily enveloped in his mother's warmth. His tiny body almost com- pletely disappeared in his mother's bushy coat.

The next time Ramti was pushed toward his food supply, he found himself lying next to a sister. She had been born during the night. Now the bear family was complete.

The sound of the axe was still echoing through Big Stream Mountain, and Akka quieted her cubs by feeding them. Fortunately she had lots of milk and the cave was cozy and warm. The only thing that disturbed the peace of the little family was the sound of that axe. The hunter was setting traps for grouse. He kept coming closer. He would ride along the river, stop to set his trap and then ride on, only to stop and chop again. Finally, toward evening, the noise stopped and a peaceful twilight settled over the mountain.

Cautiously Akka crawled up to the entrance of the lair. With her long, pointed claws she scraped away some icicles. They jingled and clanked as they plummeted down the steep precipice. Akka listened, all her senses on the alert. She stuck her head out and filled her mouth with snow. While her cubs were suckling she needed more liquid. When she looked down and saw the frothy cascade of Big Stream, she felt even more thirsty. She desperately wanted to drink, but didn't dare, for she feared that her tracks would lead the hunter directly to her lair.

For a long time she lay at the opening, enjoying the taste of the snow. Night fell and there seemed to be no sign of danger. The cubs were snug inside. The stars began to glitter on the horizon, and the frosty white moon rose beyond the black forest in the east and slowly began its nightly round. The valley and the mountain were suffused in a yellowish-white haze, except at the summit, where flashes of blue-violet streaked the treetops. The long, lonely howl of a wolf came from somewhere in the distance. An ancient, glimmering white mountain owl, who lived on the other side of the valley, gave an answering muffled hoot. When the wolf howled again, she flew out from behind her stone and up through the valley. She herself couldn't be seen, but the shadow of her wings extended from one bank of the stream to the other. The old owl was very wise and knew that there was always a dead reindeer or some other good morsel where the wolf had been.

A wail from Ramti's sister, Ramta, who had been born unusually small, called Akka back into the lair. Both cubs were fed, after which they fell asleep at the source of their food supply.

A few days later Ramti had settled upon his favorite spot—between his mother's soft, warm front paws. Where Ramta lay between feedings didn't matter to him. If they met, however, and things got crowded, he was annoyed, especially so if Ramta wailed into his ear and his mother didn't shut her up. Then he would howl in protest. Aside from that, he was more or less content with things as they were. Often he slept all day long, and after his supper he even dozed through the night. At first he was annoyed whenever his mother crept to the opening of the cave for some snow to quench her thirst. But in time he got used to it and waited patiently for her to return. She never stayed away very long.

Then one day, to his surprise, he could see, and life suddenly became more pleasant. The next day he heard a peculiar sound in the distance. It was the sound of the hunter's axe. He was setting grouse traps. As winter wore on, he worked his way farther and farther up the mountain.

Soon Ramti had grown so much in both size and strength that he decided to have a look around the world. His mother allowed him to toddle beside one of her front paws, which was much bigger than he was. For a long time he stared at her enormous claws. He made up his mind to climb over one claw, and when he had mastered that, he confidently tackled the other four.

Then he made his way across the moss to one of Akka's hind paws. There he found Ramta sleeping soundly. She didn't even wake up when he climbed over her and up onto his mother's broad flank.

Becoming increasingly bold, he continued until he

reached her back. There he stopped because he seemed to be dangerously high. As luck would have it, he stumbled and fell right on his nose, landing with a thud in the moss. Ramti was in a rage. The moss got into his snout and his face was full of dust. He snorted loudly, rubbed his eyes, but didn't whimper. For a long time he sat there just looking at the gray mud walls of the lair and the giantess, his mother, lying in the middle. He crawled up to her head, raised himself on his hind legs and peered into one of her eyes. Just then she sneezed and, in his fright, Ramti jumped sky high. As though he feared another attack of sneezing, he crept about the lair, after which he snuggled up against his mother's chest.

Since he was tired, he was very much annoyed to find Ramta in his favorite resting place. He slapped her across the snout with his paw as hard as he could. When she, to his further exasperation, didn't move an inch but only whimpered, he tried sinking his teeth in her ear until she howled with pain.

But then their mother decided it was time to intervene. She uttered a threatening growl and picked up her son by the scruff of the neck. Ramti was frightened. He didn't realize that his mother had such dangerous teeth.

Without another peep, he ate his supper and fell asleep.

Toward morning a snowstorm began which lasted for three days. There was no sound of the hunter's axe during the day and no hooting of owls or howling of wolves at night. Only the muffled sound of the storm sweeping through the valley reached the lair.

The entrance was now unprotected since Akka had eaten up most of the snow outside. Now and then whirlpools of cold, white snow came blowing in. It melted quickly, the moss became wet, and Ramti and Ramta now cuddled as close to their mother as they had when they were newborn. Their coats were still thin and they didn't like the damp and cold.

The storm reached its peak during the night. The air became warmer, and huge drifts of wet snow clung to the cliff. Gradually they loosened and went roaring down the mountain with breathtaking speed.

That night there wasn't a peaceful moment in the lair. Akka growled threateningly at the storm, and once she even flew into a rage. This was when an especially big snowslide walled up the entrance to the lair and thundered down the mountain until it hit the ice on Big Stream.

The next day they had no daylight in the lair because of the block of hard-packed snow at the entrance. Akka left it that way until the moss bed had dried. Then she started to scratch a hole in the wall.

Animated by the faint rays of daylight seeping in,

Ramti resumed his small exploratory trips across his sleeping mother or around the lair. Ramta was almost as lively, and often they frisked around together. But just as often, they fought, making such a racket that Akka, sometimes a bit brusquely, had to restore the peace. Ramti would then find himself high above the bed of moss, hanging by the scruff of his neck, held securely between his mother's strong teeth.

Despite his mother's stern reprimands, Ramti remained pretty much the same. He soon learned to know his own strength, which was far greater than his sister's. He was impatient with her when she wanted to play and he wanted to sleep. Then he would use his teeth on her, and his mother would use hers on him.

Ramti had found out that the back of his neck was sensitive, but to escape punishment wasn't easy. Their home was crowded. Akka reached the ceiling if she stood up on her hind legs, and when she stretched out, she spanned the floor from wall to wall. Therefore the lair was most comfortable when the whole family slept —which they did quite a lot. This was a gift nature had bestowed upon them all.

2. The Coming of Spring

THE precipice which descended abruptly into Big Stream had a southern exposure. Many bears had built lairs there, but this year only two of them were inhabited. The previous summer Ramti and his sister had lost their father—he had been the victim of a hunter's bullet. Two other bears had fled. A frightened young female had escaped up the valley to a higher and safer place, and an orphaned cub, who had originally come from the forests in the east, had wandered back there last autumn. The only bears remaining on top of the cliff were Ramti, his sister, Ramta, his mother, Akka, and an old male bear, Toivo, who lived near Big Stream. Old bears were always courageous and he had decided to remain in his cave, although it was so close to the hunter's trail. When he was younger he had had his lair higher up. But gradually he had learned to fool the hunters. Now he spent his time roaming around and stopping in places where he felt at home.

In mid-April the old bear had already crawled out of his winter abode. Big Stream Valley was deserted. The hunters had returned to their homes and their zigzag footprints had disappeared with the melting snow. Wolverines, wolves, and other four-footed animals, as well as birds, had retreated to the upper part of the valley where some birds of passage were also beginning to appear.

But the bear family on the cliff and the old male bear down below stayed on. Akka and the cubs were still hibernating in their cave and old Toivo had settled only a short distance from his winter home. He up-rooted a few decayed birch stubs, spread them, together with willow branches, over the snow, and lay down upon this rug to await spring. When he got bored on his hill he went back to his lair, nosed around for a bit, and then returned to his temporary quarters. His path had left large, dark stripes on the white snow between the lair and the hill. The tracks looked like a crooked line of large block letters drawn on a white sheet of paper, and he, like an enormous black ink-blot.

Now warm, sunny days were followed by cold spells, and gentle night winds from the south were swept away by severe storms from the north. But spring finally

won, and Big Stream Mountain bared more and more
of its slumbering ground. Ice floes came roaring down
the cliffs and were transformed into merry cascades of
water. Down in the valley the bare spots were continually growing larger. Bird calls increased in quantity
and volume, and the flapping wings of many migratory
birds filled the air. Some of the more delicate species
flew back south to await warmer weather, while others

continued to build nests or make their way still farther up the mountain.

One night when the first buzzards began to squabble over an old nest up on the mountain, Toivo, aroused, decided to do a little reconnaissance. A small herd of reindeer was grazing on the south slope of the valley, and he headed in that direction. But he was starting out a day too late. The ice on Big Stream, made slushy by the sun, burst under his weight when he tried to cross it. Rushing water and ice floes carried him down the stream and over a waterfall. He was growling with rage when the ruthless current forced him into a crevice. In his fury, he overturned a huge boulder that was in his way and, panting, heaved himself out of the water. By this time he was exhausted and bruised, and in a nasty mood. He shook himself vigorously trying to get the water out of his coat. For some time he stood grumbling, but eventually continued on upward through a thorny birch forest.

When he scented the reindeer he raised his head, sniffed and licked his lips. Hidden from them by jutting rocks, he emerged from the forest and continued up the mountainside. But the reindeer, having heard him roaring down in the river, were on their guard and made a hasty retreat. He lumbered slowly after them. Both the fleeing reindeer and their pursuer soon disappeared over the summit. A flock of hawks had already begun hovering over him. They, too, were eager to still their hunger with reindeer meat, and they had confidence in the old male bear, who so many times before had supplied them with food.

The same evening Akka was also awakened from her slumber by the screeching buzzards up on the mountain. Irritated, she started to climb up the incline, but, unable to reach the place where the buzzards had their nest, she turned back. She was scrawny and empty, and her teats hung limp under her belly. As she approached the lair, she stilled her worst hunger pangs with a few watery berries left over from the previous summer, and these, with some willow and mountain-ash buds, made up her meal. Then she stretched out full length beside the lair with her head between her front paws. All living creatures around her thought she was sleeping, but, on the contrary, she was very much on the alert. The time of year and the sound of the buzzards had put life into her. She was eager to go foraging for food, but the cubs confined her to the lair and the area surrounding it. For the moment she had to content herself with following the happenings in the valley with her roving eyes.

Around midnight the buzzards quieted down. But the ensuing silence was broken by the spirited spring games of the white grouse up on Big Stream Mountain as well as in the valley. A small bog which separated the mountain from the river was the scene of their frolicking. Few other birds appear to have the same happy disposition as the grouse. They seem to meet even misfortune with merriment. A family of foxes had settled in a sand hill near the bog, and every night a grouse cock, who had been chirping away only a few moments earlier, would be dragged dead or dying into the foxhole.

But the foxes also had their enemies. When a pair of wolf eyes glittered from the underbrush, the foxes would beat a hasty retreat into their hole. Sometimes at daybreak, one of the eagles who made his home the year round on Big Stream Mountain, would put in an appearance. The eagles were kings of the sky and also ruled over many earthbound creatures. Their breakfast usually consisted of grouse, but for supper they would eat the lemmings which they had gathered during the day. Lying around their nests were bleached hare and fox skeletons, or sometimes a discarded fluffy foxtail— proof that even the sly fox wasn't safe.

In the midst of this teeming animal life, the hungry bear kept watch through the night. She was the biggest and strongest of them all, but what good did that do? Even the mountain lemmings, which were going north in masses, were beyond her reach. They usually ran along the riverbank or floated on the ice floes wherever the wind or the current happened to take them. It wasn't until late that afternoon that a small lemming went astray near the bear cave. Akka grabbed at it with her enormous front paw, and in its terror the lemming tumbled backward into the lair. Now it was Ramti's and Ramta's turn to take up the chase. The lemming made a brave effort to defend himself. He kept on running around his pursuers, yelping furiously. His best defense was his wild temper, and with that he managed to confuse the cubs until he had maneuvered himself to the opening. With blood in his eye he retreated, followed by Ramti. But the little creature was so engrossed in his struggle for existence that he had completely forgotten the danger lurking outside. In a split second he was between Akka's jaws, and there his squealing stopped forever.

This morsel made Akka hungrier than ever. And, although it was still light, she went out on a short foray to look for something to eat. She made her way along the bare spots so as not to leave any tracks, and after a while she came to the sand hill where the foxes lived. Eagerly she began digging in their tunnels, ripping up roots and sand with her sharp claws. Sometimes she would stop and listen for noises inside. She could smell the foxes and hear them move; muffled sounds of growling and short yelps reached her ears. Unfortunately the foxes had burrowed too far into the hill, and Akka had to give up. Panting, she shook the

sand out of her matted coat as she lumbered down
along a brook toward the stream.

From the bank she threw herself far out into the
water and swam with the current for a while. During
the winter, fish froze to death in the shallow parts of
the stream and would drift ashore with the spring
floods.

In a thicket along the edge of the stream, she smelled rotten fish, and upon investigation she discovered it was a big salmon. And in the place where the hunter had put his traps, she found a grouse that had been left behind. Hurriedly she gathered together the remains and ran back to her lair the same way she had come.

What she saw when she arrived made her wild. During her absence, a wolverine had sneaked down the mountain. Unaware of his presence, the cubs had crawled out of the lair and were playfully romping about.

The wolverine was getting ready to attack when Akka appeared. But at her terrifying growl he quickly fled and disappeared up the steep cliffs.

The wolverine was a better climber than the bear. But Akka was now in such a rage that she couldn't give up the chase. Many times the wolverine thought he was safe on a precipice, but the bear always found a way of reaching him. Finally he was forced to retreat to a narrow crevice which went way into a rock. He squeezed himself into it, while Akka, who was much larger, had to stay outside.

Slowly she started back to her cave, the whole time keeping an eye on the crevice where she had left the wolverine. Whenever he appeared, she took a few menacing steps in his direction. This state of war con-

tinued twice round the clock, but during the darkest part of the night, the wolverine managed to flee over the mountain ridge to the south.

A few days later Toivo came back from his pursuit of the reindeer. Big Stream was now free from ice, and, with this obstacle out of the way, he threw himself into the water and swam almost all the way to his lair. On his way he stopped to visit Akka and the cubs. His hunt had obviously been successful; remains of meat and tufts of hair stuck to the long fur around his neck and whiskers. Despite this evidence of strife, he looked very peaceful sitting at a distance watching Akka and the cubs. He also made himself pleasant to Ramti, who clung to him and began tugging at his fur with his teeth and claws. He even went so far as to play with Ramti for a while. But, since he wasn't especially interested in either Akka or the cubs at that time, he didn't stay long. He was thinking of the forests in the east, where there were hundreds of ant hills containing millions of delicious ants and eggs. Slowly he waddled along the cliff in that direction.

The Lapps had now started bringing their reindeer back to the mountains. Their tents were spread around the area, and one was very close to Big Stream Mountain. During the spring months they often let their reindeer stop and graze on the plateau.

One night Akka heard the sound of a reindeer bell

tinkling up there. She climbed the cliff and fell on the herd. When she came back she carried a freshly killed reindeer calf between her teeth.

That night they had a feast in the lair.

Walpurgis night fires were crackling down in the village. The light from them became yellowish white as it rose and blended with the blue sky. The Lapps of Big Stream Valley were gathered around singing "Fresh Spring Winds." Perhaps their thoughts wafted along with the veil of smoke as it moved up the valley. But they didn't worry about their reindeer since none of them was aware of the existence of the new bear family that had come into being during the winter.

3. Akka and the Reindeer

THE beginning of May brought a heat wave which melted almost all the snow down in the wooded area, and half of the white blanket covering the mountain. Also many of the southern slopes began to turn green. Heather and willow sprouted in the crevices of Big Stream Mountain, and some sheltered birch shrubs developed tender green leaves. Where the warmth of the sun was able to reach the roots of the angelica plant and the mountain lettuce, they also began to emerge shyly. Gradually they would sprout, produce buds, and large quantities of them would end up in bear stomachs.

Greens were still scarce around the lair, and even the meat supply sometimes gave out. The vegetation took its time to produce food for bears and Akka was still too tied down by her cubs to be able to go far afield in her search for something edible. It was for this reason that she came into conflict with human beings.

Soon after the May Day festivities in the village, Sjur, one of the Big Stream Valley Lapps, returned to his herd of reindeer, where bear tracks and blood on the snow told him the whole story. Slowly and methodically he followed the tracks, which led him toward the cliff above Big Stream. He confirmed his suspicions. Now he was bent on revenge! It was impossible for him to climb down the cliff and reach the lair—it was much too steep. Besides, he didn't know the exact location. But he was going to do his utmost to get that bear.

First he gathered his herd together and drove it some distance away from Big Stream Mountain. Then he rode to his tent to fetch his gun. It was an old one, almost as old as Sjur himself. The barrel was rusted and the teeth of bears and wolves had left deep marks on the butt—souvenirs from earlier hunts. Sjur also had many battle scars, acquired before his eyes had begun to dim from years of squinting at storm-lashed or blindingly sunlit mountains. But although his eyesight was failing and he was no longer so strong and swift as he used to be, he still felt himself capable of tackling the bear who stole his reindeer. He was going to spread out a reindeer skin on the snow and keep watch from there every night.

No one was in the least apprehensive at the lair—on the contrary, the atmosphere was unusually peaceful and harmonious. The cubs still lived mostly on mother's milk and Akka's worst hunger had been stilled with meat, remains of fish, and whatever else she had found. But she was still hungry.

Unfortunately for the cubs, the play area outside the lair became too cramped for them. The cliff above was almost vertical, and about six feet from the entrance of the lair there was again a sudden drop. The only space they had on either side of the cave was just about enough to turn around in. On either side were jutting cliffs which only Akka was able to negotiate.

One day a gentle wind brought the smell of meat. Akka's whiskers began to quiver and her movements became increasingly agitated. After glancing at the cubs, who seemed to be content, she jumped up on a boulder and for a while stood sniffing the air in all directions. When she had determined where the scent came from, she stalked off in that direction. Every few paces she would stop and sniff the tantalizing aroma, which led her farther and farther afield.

Finally she arrived at a spot where one of winter's avalanches had packed together a large mass of snow, mud, rocks, trees and roots. Out of this enormous, compressed heap oozed the smell of meat. To force her way into this debris was no easy matter. But she felt compelled to tackle it. Something savory was surely buried under this avalanche.

Nothing seemed too hard for her. Her efforts to burrow into the tightly packed mass made her hungrier than ever. She began to feel uneasy about the cubs and this made her all the more frantic. She grabbed a huge tree stump between her paws and violently wrenched it out. A big stone loosened and went crashing down in the other direction. With these obstacles out of the way, she managed to dig herself through a heavy layer of mud and underbrush. The smell of meat was everywhere but she didn't find a thing. After a quick look at the heap from another angle she lumbered back home, downcast and disappointed. She just couldn't stay away from the cubs any longer.

But she couldn't settle down at home. The delicious smell of meat still clung to her nostrils. She became still more agitated that evening when the breeze brought the scent of live reindeer and with it the enticing tinkling of reindeer bells.

During the long twilight she lay looking up toward the summit. Then it got too much for her and she started climbing in the direction of the reindeer.

Stealthily she approached the scattered herd. She was just about to leap at a fat reindeer bull when the sound of human footsteps made her stop. A Lapp girl carrying a stick came walking around the herd; Sjur had been joined by other Lapps. Akka hid behind a stone, cautiously watching. The Lapp girl was sitting

down and the only part of her that was visible was the tip of her cap, which stuck up from behind a hillock. Farther away a small fire was burning. Two people were standing beside it. For a long while Akka waited patiently. Finally the Lapp girl went toward the fire.

But now Sjur began making the rounds! He had long hair and a beard and was dressed in a long coat of reindeer skins. At a distance he looked more like an animal than a man. But Akka knew that it was a human being by the sound of his peaked boots. Besides, he was walking on two feet and he smelled of man. She snorted when the unpleasant odor reached her nostrils. Sjur heard the snort and looked in the direction of the stone behind which Akka was hiding. He began to shout, waved his arms and made peculiar noises. A man came running. For a while the bear was torn between the desire to attack, remain where she was, and try to chase some reindeer down the cliff. She ended up by heedlessly running down the mountainside to get away from all the commotion.

By now she was so hungry that she headed straight for the avalanche. Throughout the night she worked so hard that steam rose around her. Now, if ever, she had to eat her fill!

Toward morning she finally found the meat and scratched it out. It was a reindeer that had been over-taken by the avalanche. The carcass was still fresh and solidly frozen. No spring warmth had penetrated the tightly packed mass. Akka spent a long time on the tasty carcass. Then she gathered up the remains and hid them in the same place. She took with her only a front leg with an attached shoulder—that was all she could carry down the precipice.

These were happy days at the lair. Every night Akka went up to the avalanche to fetch more food, and every day she spent playing with her cubs. The reindeer meat had done her a lot of good. She had gained weight and was beginning to look like herself again. Her teats shrank together to the sorrow of the cubs, but in time they also learned to appreciate the reindeer meat.

Of the two cubs, Ramti ate the most and grew the fastest. He was now about the size of a small dog. Along his back and sides his fur was a glossy dark brown, and his belly and legs were pitch black. His most unusual feature was a ring of white hair around his neck. This made him unusually colorful for a bear, but he was still handsome.

The mountain buzzards had stopped quarreling and each couple did their best to build a nest on their rocky pinnacle. The feared golden eagle made an occasional dive toward their nests, but only once did he succeed in overtaking a sleeping male buzzard. When awake, the buzzards were extremely alert. Sometimes they would band together and attack the big one up there.

That was always an exercise in air warfare. The eagle kept on soaring upward on his broad wings. He had the ability to fly higher than the buzzards and wanted to keep the attackers below him. He wasn't afraid of them, but he didn't care for their lightning dives on his back.

Big Stream Valley was still free from human beings. The waters swelled with the coming of spring, and the roar of the foaming falls thundered against the cliffs. In other, more peaceful places, the whole flooded valley lay like a lake, with only the higher willows and birches visible. Every evening some long-legged moose would wade around feeding on the sprouting vegetation.

Up on the mountain there were people. The calls of the Lapps and the barking of dogs could be heard from time to time. But at this season the Lapps were particularly quiet; it was the time when their herds increased and they didn't want to disturb the cows and the calves more than necessary.

During clear, peaceful nights the sound of Lapp songs would come floating all the way down Big Stream Mountain. Akka pricked up her ears and listened. Many of the sounds the Lapps made reminded her of the howling of wolves. The sounds were unpleasant but they didn't frighten her. She was still safe here on her cliff, and her courage increased as the snow melted and the bare spots grew larger in the valley below.

One day she brought home the last of the carcass she had buried in the avalanche. When it was gone she began to sniff around, and again ventured up the mountain. She had to find something because so far the vegetation didn't yield much that was edible. The reindeer up there were her one hope.

One night when fog and heavy, gray rain-laden clouds swept over the mountain moors she made her way up to where the reindeer were grazing. She knew she had to hide her large body or the reindeer would take flight. She hid in a hollow that the brook had scooped out of the ground. From there she watched some reindeer coming toward her. She lay still, waiting. The reindeer, oblivious of her presence, began to drink. This was the moment she had been waiting for!

Akka dug her claws into the ground, leaped, and landed next to the closest reindeer. A second later it was her prey.

During the darkest part of the night she was left in peace and enjoyed her meal as only a healthy bear can. But toward dawn there appeared—as too often before —an uninvited guest at her table. This time it was a blue Arctic fox. He kept on making circles around her and gradually closing in.

Akka was very much annoyed. What right did he have to disturb her? The fox sat down on its bushy tail and licked its lips in anticipation. He even had the nerve to yap at her. And when she replied with a threatening growl, he let out such an unpleasant howl that she completely lost her temper. She had to get rid of that parasite; otherwise she would have no peace. She took off after him, but, just as she was about to catch the blue brute, he disappeared into a foxhole. To penetrate this labyrinth of hundreds of passageways was impossible. She stayed for a while waiting for the fox to emerge, and then she lumbered back to her feeding place.

But the blue fox wasn't the only one who had scented the lavish new food supply. Akka came back just in time to see another fox run off with a piece of the reindeer between his teeth. She was just about to set out in hot pursuit after this new parasite when she suddenly stiffened and remained motionless.

A heavy scent of tobacco and man filled the air. Tensely she listened, with her head cocked to one side. She heard a vague crunching of snow beyond the next hill, and suddenly she saw Sjur's cap. That was more than enough to set her into action. Hastily she made her way back to Big Stream Mountain and leaped down it. Now that her stomach was full, her fear of human beings returned.

The following night she again made her way up the mountain. The thoughts of leftover reindeer proved irresistible. Everything had been so quiet up there during the day that she decided to risk it. Still, she was on her guard as she approached her prey.

The carcass had been by then practically gnawed to the bone by other scavengers, mostly foxes, buzzards and hawks. Bits of reindeer hide were strewn all over the mountain, and a pungent smell of excrement from various visitors disguised the scent of human beings.

Akka decided it was time to clean up around her table. She mustered her courage and carried the carcass to a secluded place at the edge of a spring.

Most of the night was peaceful and uneventful as Akka was savoring the reindeer, drinking from the spring and feeling at ease. The sky was clear and the air, chilly. The cold had caused a thin layer of ice to form on the spring, and even Akka's fur was frosted. Now and then she brushed away the rime from her long eyelashes and scanned the area for disturbers of the peace who might have discovered her. When she had assured herself that she was alone, her interest again turned back to her delicious repast.

But suddenly the silence was broken by a resounding rifle shot. It echoed along the plateau, resounded against the cliffs, boomeranged and floated off into the distance. Hundreds of grouse cocks raised their voices in jubilation. But Akka didn't see any cause for rejoicing. A bullet had landed in the spring right next to her.

A cascade of ice and water almost blinded her.

Heedlessly she got up and ran, not knowing where. She was oblivious to everything except fear that the spring, perhaps the whole mountain, was about to explode.

More shots were fired, each as terrifying as the first one. The mountain echoed with rifle fire. In the midst of all this noise Akka met Sjur face to face for the first time. In her dazed state she ran right into him. He fumbled with his rifle, managed to reload it and shoot, but again he missed.

Terrified, Akka continued her flight. She darted across the mountain and then made a wide swing back toward Big Stream Valley. As she ran, she regained her acute perception and sense of danger. As she approached the cliff she could see Sjur standing guard at the spot where she usually climbed down to her lair. She made an about-face and ran along the mountain plateau.

Only at daybreak did she stop, on a high peak where she had a clear view from every angle. It was a long time before she dared to move.

She was both terrified and defiant as she lay there watching, and she felt an overwhelming desire to get back to her lair.

But the fear of Sjur and the bullets gained the upper hand. She had to wait for a while before she dared venture home.

4. The Eagle

ON A sunny spring day Ramti awoke, crawled outside, and yawned at the whole world. He was soon joined by Ramta. Akka was away but neither of them showed much concern—they had become used to it. They spent most of their time sleeping or playing and were often surprised when their mother appeared outside the lair.

There were still some dirty, although tasty bits of food lying about, and when they had eaten their fill, Ramti tackled a job which had kept him busy for quite a few days and which he couldn't seem to finish.

He was working away at a birch root which was blocking the entrance to a crevice which he was very anxious to reach. Sometimes he would tear long splinters from the root and then dig out the earth around it. He also tried to wrench it out by force, but when he failed, he became furious and bit it. Then he looked longingly into the crevice, which smelled of lemming and field mouse and held the promise of many other good things. But he couldn't budge that root.

This struggle often put him in a foul temper. Dusty, sweaty, and most of all thirsty, he would leave the place growling. It was then that he missed his mother most of all if she happened to be away. There wasn't a single patch of snow left outside the lair and not a drop of water to quench his thirst. The only available liquid was his mother's milk.

Since he had used up most of his energy on the root and his mother wasn't around, he began playing with his sister. As usual it put him back in good spirits. In front of the lair there was another birch, tall and slender, and the first one to reach the tree could scramble up into it and swing for a while. The other one would follow and their combined weight would make the birch bend down to the ground. Both of them then lost their footing and went tumbling around as the birch snapped back. The cubs never tired of the game and went through the motion many times before they gave up.

By then more than half the day was gone. The sun was still beating against the cliffs, but gradually it slipped behind the ridges in the west. The valley already lay in shadows and the evening birds began to come out to hunt. The female buzzards were still hatch-

ing their eggs, but the males were very active. From
time to time one of them would dive down into the
underbrush and come up clutching a small creature
which only a few seconds before had been alive. Lemmings especially would be caught on their first and last
flight. The buzzards weren't particularly interested in
pursuing birds. Sometimes a grouse or a wild duck
would be carried off to the buzzards' nests, but most
often it would be an ailing or an already dead bird.

The cubs lay dozing in the pale light of the evening
sun and followed the birds with their eyes. Ramti was
almost asleep when he was suddenly awakened by a
violent buzzing right above him. The next second a
large golden eagle was standing on the platform in
front of the lair.

The cubs couldn't escape inside because the menacing eagle was blocking their way. As he approached
them he puffed up his feathers. Ramti growled and
bared as many of his teeth as he could. That resistance
made the eagle think twice. For a long time he stood
there with his head raised and his wings spread, swaying
forth and back. A gurgling sound came from his curved
beak and his eyes were flaming with rage. He held this
position until he saw his opportunity to attack.

Ramti felt a stinging blow on the back of his neck.
But at the same time he struck at the eagle with his
paw, and when the eagle let go, Ramti bit one of his

legs. For a moment the two tumbled about but the eagle soon spread its wings and soared away. Taken by surprise, Ramti let go his grip and landed with a hard bang practically on the same spot where he had just been standing. The next instant the eagle was back. A golden eagle doesn't give up that quickly.

For the moment, he left Ramti alone. But he attacked Ramta. Courageously she tried to defend herself, but she wasn't convincing enough. When the eagle moved toward her, flapping his wings, she stumbled backward—exactly what the eagle wanted her to do. Unaware of the danger, she backed closer and closer to the abyss. Her whole attention was focused on the eagle. He now felt himself to have the upper hand and became increasingly bold. His broad wings flapped uninterruptedly and were like an impenetrable screen between her and the lair. Finally she stood on the brink of the precipice, and with the next attack she tumbled backward into the ravine.

The eagle flew away in pursuit of her and Ramti quickly retreated inside the lair. Whimpering with terror he curled up in a corner. Never before had he been this frightened. He was also hungry. There was food outside but he didn't dare go near it. Even though it was beginning to get dark, he left the food untouched. The eagle might come back.

It was a sad night for Ramti. His neck ached from

the eagle's bite. His sister had fallen down the precipice and his mother was away. . . .

Hesitating, Akka slowly approached Big Stream Mountain. Blue and white mountain foxes soundlessly slipped away when they saw her. They looked like tiny shadowy spots against the billowing whiteness of the mountain. Eight wolves walking in a row appeared more distinctly, but they soon faded into the darkness.

A couple of hundred of Sjur's reindeer were grazing in a depression on the mountain. From a distance the herd looked like a craggy bare spot. But it moved, changed shape, and sometimes seemed to sway back and forth—that was when a dog came too close. Sounds of Lapp voices came from around the herd.

Akka stopped and listened for a while, but then she trudged on.

Part of the reindeer carcass was still left. A red fox was sitting there gorging himself. Akka saw him as well as the carcass, but tonight she made a wide detour around it. She had a painful memory of the previous night's shooting, splashing of water, flashes of lightning and the smell of gunpowder right at that spot. She would never again go near there!

As she reached the crest of Big Stream Mountain she got a whiff of man and smoke. Nevertheless, defiantly she continued on to the place where she could

get down to her lair. But just before she reached it, she stopped short. Next to some embers lay a man snoring. It was Sjur. He had settled down there to await Akka's return, but the waiting had become too long and he had fallen sound asleep. After Akka had watched him for a while, she lumbered off.

Her usual path down to the lair was blocked. She would have to go around the cliff. It was a detour of almost a mile and filled with piles of stone, steep slopes, and ravines. But once she had made up her mind she increased her pace and finally reached her home, where she was welcomed by Ramti in the manner of bears.

But one was missing! Her feeling of oneness with the little ones told her that something was wrong. She knew it with a mother's instinct. She went out and began to look around. She looked in the tree where the cubs used to play, in the crevice where Ramti used to work; she combed the area. She went in and out of the lair and finally she climbed up the cliff and went out to the edge of the precipice. There she stood for a long time, sniffing and looking straight down.

Later that day she carried Ramti from cliff to cliff down Big Stream Mountain. When they reached more even ground, Ramti toddled behind her down toward the valley. By sniffing her way she finally found her other cub. But it was only a mangled, lifeless body. The eagle had more than triumphed. Their life at the lair had come to an end.

Akka turned the dead body over with her paw. For a long time she stood still, sniffing and looking at it. Then she carried it to a hole and raked some dead leaves and moss over it.

Swaying slightly she walked with Ramti toward the forests which lay behind Big Stream Valley.

5. Ramti's First Summer

THE summer promised to be a good one in the pine forest. The cuckoo crowed on the hills and the cranes called out from the swamps and marshes. Cloudberry blossoms and violets adorned the landscape, which was populated by all kinds of wild creatures and tame ones, too.

The animals of the village were now grazing in the forest. The horses had been gathered together in large numbers and now occupied a whole mountain. They would gallop wildly back and forth trying to escape the flies and mosquitoes. But sometimes they also ran for joy, the joy of being free.

Cattle were a rare sight in these mountains. Conditions were too violent for them. They preferred to be closer to the village. The tinkling of sheep and goat bells could be heard all around the village, but only the goats would faithfully make their way back to the barn every night.

In this new area there were plenty of berries from the previous season, and for a while Akka and Ramti lived primarily off these. Later on they found a dead moose in a bog. Akka moved quickly to safeguard this delicious find. Soon she had dragged the moose high up on a hill which became the table of the bear family. It wasn't every day that chance yielded such a feast.

There were also other bears in the big forest. The strongest and most enterprising of them was old Toivo, who had left Big Stream Valley the previous spring to come down here. He had traveled far and wide since then and had lots of accomplishments to his credit. In his wake he had left a trail of broken ant hills whose inhabitants were working frantically to repair their dwellings before the return of the frost. This being the beginning of the mating period, Toivo was strolling idly around with a young female, Saivva, whom he had won from a weaker male bear.

One day they happened to come by where Akka and Ramti were staying. They were hungry, and in a short time most of the moose had disappeared into their stomachs. After that Toivo wanted to renew his acquaintance with Akka, but was quickly put in his place. Nature hadn't prepared her for bearing more young this coming winter.

At a distance Ramti watched his mother and Toivo settle their affairs. It took him quite a while before he dared go up to them. He looked in astonishment at the giant. Despite the fact that he was of the same race and sex, this colossus was at least twenty times as heavy as he was. Even his mother seemed small and uninteresting compared to this towering visitor. The ground gave way under his feet and his claws ripped up the moss as he walked. When the stranger yawned, Ramti could almost have crawled in between the broad jaws.

To get acquainted, Ramti playfully bit the giant's tail and gave a good tug. But old Toivo didn't think that was funny. Far from it! At the moment he had no interest in male bears. With a furious movement he turned around to grab the culprit. When Ramti in his terror clung to the stump of tail, both of them flew around in circles. Finally something gave way and Ramti stumbled headlong down the hill. When he finally got on his feet again, dizzy and confused, he was spitting out the remains of Toivo's hairless tail. Luckily for Ramti, Akka came to his rescue; otherwise things might have gone badly for him. Toivo just sat there giving him black, menacing looks. Toivo's snarls became downright terrifying if Ramti happened to go near Saivva or in the vicinity of the reindeer. Sometimes Ramti had to flee for his life to escape Toivo's powerful paws. He would usually climb a tree since he was faster than old Toivo and felt safe up there.

Since he wasn't allowed to eat the reindeer meat, Ramti began to fish for frogs in the swamp and in the little stream which led off from it. He would lie or slowly crawl along the edge and quickly snap up all frogs that jumped out of the water. He seldom tried to catch them in the water; that was much too difficult.

One day the reindeer meat gave out. When the previous year's berries finally had been eaten and there were no more frogs in the swamp, the bears had to move on. Toivo went first, closely followed by his chosen one. Akka followed at a short distance, and Ramti brought up the rear. He preferred to keep as great a distance as possible between himself and fierce old Toivo. Of course, there was a shortage of food in the rear, but he had no choice. He did manage to make a few small forays on his own, so he wasn't too badly off.

The bears were not making a major move; they were only trying to get a bit closer to the village. The fact that Toivo headed in this direction could have been a coincidence, but he may also have planned it. Besides, he hadn't invited anyone except Saivva to follow him.

The summer nights were now as bright as the summer days. Many mountain peaks had sunshine around the clock, and even the dense forest never became dark.

The shepherds in the village would have had a wonderful life if it hadn't been for the bears. The sheep rarely made their way back to their pens at night. When the weather was dry, they settled on the soft ground wherever they happened to be, and when it rained, they sought shelter under some dense spruce or a jutting cliff.

One beautiful night the bear procession approached one of these flocks. Toivo immediately began stalking his prey. A few stealthy paces, a long leap and a blow with his paw brought down the sheep with the bell. The others bleated in terror and dispersed, like chaff in the wind. They tried to get home but some never did. Toivo was ferocious and was helped by the other bears. When the hunt was over there were four dead sheep lying along a small path.

The bear feast that followed didn't last long. Early the following morning two hunters carrying rifles came into the forest. They had dogs with them who ran in wide circles, barking and making a terrible racket. The situation became very unpleasant for the bears and it was now their turn to flee. As the sheep had dispersed at the onslaught of the bears, so the bears now dispersed in their flight from dogs and men.

Fortunately all of them got away with their lives—thanks to the dogs, who had warned them that the men were approaching. Luckily for Akka and Ramti, the dogs surrounded Toivo, whose ferocious temper made his flight a bit slow. He stopped for quite a while at a fallen spruce to break off branches and roots which he hurled at his antagonists. His roars echoed through the forest. By then Akka and Ramti had fled far from the scene of action, but they could hear the great bear's gallant struggle. Finally he, too, was able to shake his pursuers and came plodding along.

The bears' flight took them far away. But, true to their nature, they couldn't forget the delectable car-casses they had left behind. Akka and Ramti, who had traveled the greatest distance, were drawn back day by day, as if by a magnet, toward the place where the sheep had been killed. One night they boldly went all the way.

Toivo had already been there and, together with many hawks, had devoured most of the sheep. There were also traces of Saivva on the scene, although she had now left both the carcasses and her husband. Her desertion had to a certain extent dampened the old fellow's fighting spirit. But he was still hostile toward Ramti, which would eventually have grave conse-quences.

Since Akka was anxious to stay near the remains of the sheep and Ramti, out of fear of Toivo, didn't dare come forward, he began to make extended excursions on his own. One day he found himself in the middle of a herd of grazing cattle. They took him for an ordinary dog and attacked him from all sides. He had all he could do to get away from them. They mooed, he growled and there was a terrible scene.

A woodsman walking through the fields heard the bedlam. He hurried up to the cows and to his surprise discovered the small bear.

Instantly his mind was at work making plans. He would try to catch the bear alive, take it home and sell it to the Stockholm zoo!

Cautiously he approached from behind. Throwing himself with all his weight over Ramti, he pushed his nose into the ground. For a while Ramti lost consciousness. When he came to, his jaws were bound together with the man's belt. Even his paws had been shackled, and life at that moment was unbearable. Desperately twisting and turning, he tried with all his might to keep himself from being hoisted onto the man's shoulders, but in vain. Soon he was sitting on the woodsman's broad back staring furiously at his neck.

First the man ran through the woods until he came to a narrow path. There he had to rest for a while because, although his burden wasn't exactly heavy, it was hard to manage. The whole time Ramti kept kicking him with his bound legs and fought savagely to regain his freedom.

The man stopped only briefly and kept looking back

toward the forest. Although bears do not usually attack human beings, it could happen—especially now. The mother bear would surely follow him. That thought made the man cast uneasy glances backward while he was heading for the village.

Green fields and houses appeared between the trees. A newly decorated maypole had been raised in front of a barn, and the white church pointed its spires toward the sky. Some children were playing and bathing down at Big Stream. Cocks were crowing and hens were cackling. Summer was at its height in the village.

Terrified, Ramti was brought closer and closer to this noise, jogging along on the man's shoulders.

Then the mother bear appeared. The man, the kidnapper, instantly dropped Ramti. He didn't even give himself time to retrieve his belt, with which he had bound Ramti. He could have used it though, for, in trying to escape from the enraged mother bear, he almost lost his pants while leaping over a stone fence. He managed to get to a sheep pen, into which he darted and banged the door behind him.

Akka gave up the pursuit when she had recovered her adventurous son. She freed him from his shackles with a few quick bites. She was angry but also frightened. Never before had she been so close to human dwellings, and she wouldn't have been here now if her maternal instinct hadn't impelled her.

As always when she sensed danger, she fled. Now the feeling was stronger than ever. Therefore she ran as far away as she could. She left Big Stream Valley behind and sought her way up toward the mountains in the north. To reach them she had to cross a broad mountain ridge. Ramti toddled behind her. She had to carry him over the larger rivers and streams, but otherwise he managed by himself.

It was a distance of several miles and took a long time. But finally she reached her destination—Beaver Stream Valley.

Through the valley flowed a calm, deep stream with steep banks covered with underbrush. The bears soon discovered that the whole valley was full of this underbrush and densely growing birches, alder, mountain ash and willow trees. There was no path through the valley and no boats along the shore. It was pure wilderness, rarely crossed by human beings. The people who lived farther along the stream and mountain wanderers called this valley "the mountain jungle" and were afraid of it.

Beaver Valley formerly had been a center of beaver activity and still was, except that now it was inhabited by a new tribe. During the past century the old beaver stock had died out, and another family had settled there. Again the valley had acquired some industrious settlers. They built dams which were practically wiped out every year by the spring floods. Despite that, the beavers felt at home. Along the banks they had built their conical huts of brushwood which they used as winter dwellings.

Akka and Ramti also felt very much at home in the

valley. On the slopes between the mountains and the stream, there was an abundant growth of angelica and mountain lettuce. As summer progressed the cloud-berries ripened, as did other berries in the valley. Neither of them tasted meat but they did not miss it as their food supply was so ample.

They stayed where they were until autumn, when they decided to return to Big Stream Mountain and reclaim their old home.

Akka lay outside her lair awaiting the first winter snow. At the least sign of danger, she was prepared to leave this lair and find or dig another one. She had to have a snug and sheltered winter home because of Ramti. Therefore she had made her way here before the snow came, so that her tracks wouldn't lead the hunter to her winter abode.

Every day brought new transformations in nature. Frosty nights and stormy days plucked wilting leaves from the trees. The angelica bush shed its frozen brown leaves, braced itself defiantly against the wind, but finally bowed in resignation. At the same time the frost took the mountain lettuce, the sorrel and the monks-hood. Most of the vegetation was buried when gales of wind swept through, moving earlier deposits of leaves.

Autumn marked the mountain heath in yet another way. The frost spread its colors like paint from a palette. Its beauty was striking but fleeting. The migra-

tory birds saw and sensed it. Gradually they said good-bye to the mountains until another year. The mountain buzzards were no longer heard, and cranes and geese gathered in large V formations for their flight southward. The young eagles were the last to leave.

Then came the snow and the first wolf howls of autumn.

Akka shook her shaggy coat, happy and free from fear. There were no tracks to her lair. Even Ramti dusted off his white collar and dark coat, licked his paws, yawned and moved closer to the lair. He was as chubby as his mother and almost as lazy. He went back to the birch root, which he had attacked with such energy in the spring, and found that he could wrench it out in one fell swoop. After he had had a look around the crevice, he sank into his winter lethargy.

The stormy blue waters of Big Stream were already churning ice in its waterfalls. The defiant stream was still etching inky black lines through the valley, now silenced by winter. Willows were barren and bowed down by heavy snow along the shores. But the water in the stream still flowed.

Getting drowsier by the day, the bears watched the changes take place in the valley. Everything happened gradually and haltingly. The bears also hesitated between crawling into the lair or lying and dozing at the entrance.

One day Toivo came striding up the valley. He went to his lair, where he had spent the previous winter, and began carrying moss from a cold spring to make himself a new bed for the coming period of hibernation. But the very next day he received his eviction notice. Two hunters had tracked him down. Luckily, when Toivo ran away, the hunters also disappeared. He headed back toward the forests in the east, where the ground was still free from snow. There he would be able to arrange a resting place without leaving telltale tracks.

There were no further disturbances. Shortly thereafter, one of winter's severe snowstorms came sweeping across the valley. Akka and Ramti crawled into the lair, where they rested peacefully and dreamed away the whole winter.

6. Ramti's Second Spring

AFTER almost seven months, Akka and Ramti began to feel fully rested. Both got up and went outside. Momentous changes had taken place in Big Stream Valley. Avalanches had again descended along the valley slopes, demolishing trees and ripping up new roots. Down by the river were the hunters' traps, but there wasn't much left of them, and the hunters had returned to the village. Spring was approaching with its warmth and light, sprouting vegetation, and birdsong.

The day the bear family emerged, the sun was shining in a cloudless sky. The warmth of the sun gradually broke the winter stillness that had covered Big Stream Mountain. Water from melted ice trickled among the rocks. Large and small ice floes loosened and came careening down the mountain, leaving bare spots in their wake. The time of hope and promise had come, even for the bears. They felt a surge of new life and immediately became active.

In a nearby ravine the ground was still completely covered with snow, but free from rocks and other impediments. Akka went there, followed by Ramti. After she had stood looking down for a while, she sat down on her broad backside and slid down the steep slope toward the valley. It didn't take Ramti long to copy her. When they met at the bottom, they climbed up and went through the same motion again. This time they increased their speed and, with every ride, it grew smoother. Soon they had made a deep groove, very much like that of a toboggan slope. All they had to do to slide down was to sit or lie, sometimes on their backs, sometimes on their bellies, and sometimes they rolled downhill like great big balls.

This was a great game—especially for Ramti. But it also served another purpose. During the long slumber their fur had become matted and dirty. Now they were being washed and combed at the same time, and got some much needed exercise as well.

The following day Ramti slid down the slope innumerable times while Akka lay watching. She was also looking around for something to eat. Both she and Ramti were hungry. The long winter fast had made them thin and rangy. There were not many lemmings around and no fallen deer hidden·in an avalanche. Nor was it possible to go out hunting. The snow was too deep and difficult to negotiate around Big Stream Mountain.

Therefore their life, at least the first week after they woke up, consisted of sliding down the slope and continuing to rest in their lair. When their stomachs howled with hunger, they would gnaw at birch twigs and fibrous roots. Neither of them got fat on that diet.

Then once again, the Lapps returned to the mountains with their reindeer. As usual, they made a stop on the precipice above Big Stream and, as was her habit, Akka started to climb higher and nearer. The scent of reindeer whetted her appetite. Ramti was able to toddle along for short distances, but he couldn't get up the mountain; it was too craggy and icy.

This spring the Lapps watched their herds closely. No bear had disturbed them yet, but the wolves were bold, which meant that they were starving. Therefore Sjur had hired two young men who took turns watching the reindeer day and night.

Every night Akka climbed up on the cliff and looked in the direction of the reindeer. But there was smoke rising from the mountain, and there were small fires and the glow of embers everywhere. The reindeer grazed nearby, kept closely together. Sometimes dark shadows would appear in the distance between the mountain peaks. The wolves were darting back and forth, howling and yelping. They were aware that human beings were close to the reindeer and therefore they kept their distance.

Both Akka and the wolves were waiting in hope that a small segment of the herd—or at least one of them— would stray away from the others. But the guards carefully prevented such a thing from happening.

The spring nights became lighter and longer, and when it no longer got dark at all, the wolves stopped howling. The flocks had been so well guarded that the wolves had given up hope. Their roving instinct made them restless, and they didn't want to wait around any longer.

One night some time later, Akka went up the mountain for the last time. Several shots were fired up there that night. The following night Ramti waited in vain for his mother. She never came back. For several days Ramti waited, lonely and patient. But finally hunger drove him out of the lair.

The spruce forests in the east looked like large blue-gray waves against the horizon. To Ramti they seemed safer than the mountains at this time of year. Instinct told him that there must be some large bare spots over there. After sitting looking at the forests for a while, he began to walk in that direction.

En route he came across Toivo's tracks. He had ap-

parently started up the mountain, but turned back
when the going became too difficult. As it was easier to
walk in his tracks, Ramti followed them.

At the edge of a small mountain lake he stopped. A
flock of grouse were frolicking about on the ice. Ramti
thought it looked like fun and wanted very much to
play with them. But when he stepped out on the ice,
he soon found himself alone. The black grouse were
more frightened than amused by his presence.

He kept on following Toivo's tracks, and during the
night he entered the forest. The bare spots were getting
larger all the time. He stopped for a while and ate the
previous year's berries, which had begun to thaw.

But Toivo was ahead of him and there weren't too
many berries left so he didn't stop for very long. Rain
began to pour. Ramti arrived at a large stream, which
he had to swim across and which made his fur wetter
than ever. Soaked and miserable, he finally rolled up
under a big spruce.

Toward evening he rose and forged ahead without
any definite goal. A wood grouse had laid some eggs
beneath a pile of wood and he ate them, licking his lips
with obvious pleasure. Suddenly he became aware of a
large flock of birds of a kind he had never seen before.
These large, dark birds were sitting in the trees chatting away in their language, and Ramti couldn't help
listening to them.

At dawn all the birds gathered on a snowdrift, where they hopped, fluttered around, and acted as if they were playing hide-and-seek. Ramti ran up to them wanting to join in the fun. But none of the birds wanted to play with him. He didn't catch one, either. They all flew away.

Furious, Ramti crushed a big tree stub and he found some delicious larvae. A big black woodpecker howled shrilly when the stub was destroyed; she had intended it for her nest. After Ramti had left, she looked at the ruins for a long time before she and her mate began to build a nest in another stub.

During Ramti's aimless meandering, he suddenly perceived a peculiar mixture of smells composed of elk, fox, bear, hawk, and all kinds of animals of the forest. He increased his pace, walking against the wind, and soon reached a spot where another bear was having a feast on the carcass of an elk. The bear, a smallish male with glistening black fur and gray temples, proved to be kind as well as generous. He walked off, leaving the remains to Ramti.

Since there was a lot left of the elk and the forest was peaceful, Ramti remained where he was for quite a long time. It was only when the frogs began to croak and jump around in the marshes that he was tempted to move on. The capture of frogs gave him the nourishment he needed. Besides, it was nice to lie around on a hill, doing nothing.

The only thing Ramti lacked was playmates. But he found some—at least for a short time.

He had been surprised by a sudden snowstorm and had settled down on a mossy hillock next to a swamp, where he fell asleep. He was awakened with a start by a snowball which landed on his snout and rolled on. Another snowball hit his ear. Both irritated and playful, he jumped up and tried to catch the snowballs, which were coming from the thicket nearby.

Since they kept on coming, he finally went into the underbrush to find out where they came from. There he came face to face with two tall men who stood there laughing at him. For a second Ramti didn't move. But by now he was so playful that all fear left him. One of the men had a camera that went "click" all the time. This captured Ramti's attention and he went up and sniffed at both the men and the camera.

A happy time followed—at least for Ramti. The men wouldn't let go of the camera, and Ramti wanted it badly. He raised himself on two feet and tugged at the men's clothes while they pulled his wet, shaggy coat. Sometimes the three of them wrestled at once. Ramti was rested, he had had a good meal and was full of fun, and the men were big, strong and playful —for the time being.

But finally they tired of Ramti's increasingly violent games. For one thing, their clothes weren't strong enough to withstand Ramti's teeth and claws. They gave him a small shoulder-strap bag, which they hung up in a tree, and while Ramti stood batting it, they walked away.

7. Ramti and Toivo

Big Stream was formed by many brooks and small rivulets whose crooked furrows reached out all over the mountain. Down below they wound through the birch forest and formed small glens. During the summer the flora was always plentiful in the glens as well as in the valley. There was also a great variety of animals. The area was a vast green labyrinth inhabited by a teeming animal life.

The many animals, however, lived at the expense of one another, and daily struggles of life and death occurred in every tiny glen. The battle cries rose or descended, depending upon where the combatants were fighting. Birds would fight in the air, while four-footed animals stood down below watching. And every minute a battle was being waged on the ground, which in turn was watched from above. But in the green valleys there was also much friendship and love and peaceful family life. Nature seemed to strike a balance between war and peace.

Above the timberline, the number one songbird of the mountains, the plover, was mating. He delivered his songs in fragile, crystal-clear voice. The plover is a rather curious bird. After the young hatch, the male soon finds himself alone, for during the early part of the summer, the female moves back south and leaves all responsibility for the family in his hands. His closest kinsman is the heather plover, not nearly so handsome in plumage or voice, but more numerous and more amusing.

There was also the dotterel, the ace flyer. He couldn't hold his own as a singer, but was superb in the air. When other birds joined in a unanimous song of joy, he would rise upward with glides and swirls. Few could avoid seeing him, and many beaks were silenced in admiration.

Further down in the glens there were so many different species of birds that no one knew them all.

Around midsummer, Ramti arrived in this verdant region bursting with life. On his way, he had run into Toivo, and since then they had stuck together. When food became scarce in one glen, they would move to another, where they would again find an abundant sup-

ply of angelica and mountain lettuce. There were at least a hundred similar spots, and even if there were other bears around, there was always enough for all.

The summer was a happy time for them. Toivo grew fat and lazy and would often withdraw in order to sleep. At such times he wanted to be undisturbed; to wake him could be dangerous. Otherwise he was good-

natured and gentle, but never playful. Ramti made
many efforts to put some life into the old fellow, but
he constantly met with rebuffs.

As summer wore on, even he began to feel lazier
than usual. He had become too fat to be able to move
around easily. He even began to feel grown up. Only
once did he get carried away by a desire to romp, and
that almost had a bad ending.

One day a group of mountain hikers came through
a glade in the thorny valley. They were gaily dressed,
and Ramti was seized with an urge to have a closer
look at the most colorful one. Toivo ran away, but
Ramti walked up to the hikers. When they, to his de-
light, began to run and scream, he didn't hesitate to
take up the chase. With lightning speed they raced
through the forest and down to the banks of Big
Stream, where a boat lay anchored in a calm cove.

The men quickly jumped into the boat. But when
Ramti wanted to do likewise, he got such a hard whack
with an oar that he fell backward into the water. Then
he was beaten as never before. As soon as he was able,
he crawled out of the water and ran back to Toivo. He
ached all over. Finally he had realized that human beings just couldn't be played around with. He was glad
to see them row away.

For several days he limped around feeling miserable.
One of his front paws bothered him most. A claw had

been broken off close to the flesh. In the struggle at
the boat he had also lost a tooth. His jaw ached, and
to get rid of the pain, he often shook his head. He had
learned his lesson—stay away from human beings. For
the time being he kept close to Toivo.

Toward the end of August the leaves of the mountain lettuce and the angelica turned bitter. Plants that
were in the shade began to wilt. Since the bears weren't
very hungry at this time, they needed more tempting
food to stimulate their appetite. They found it in several swamps around the valley, which glimmered with
ripe, red cloudberries. Here there were no human beings to disturb them or pick the berries, and the supply lasted until a frosty night came and finished them
off.

It was really Toivo who was the provider. He was
in the habit of eating reindeer meat at least part of
every autumn. If he was lucky enough to find dead
reindeer, he was pleased, but otherwise he would attack living animals. During the mushroom season it
was always easy to find game. The reindeer would then
wander away from the mountain plateau and down to
the birch forest, where all a beast of prey had to do was
to lie in the underbrush and wait until a reindeer appeared in search of mushrooms. Toivo had a big,
clumsy body that was hard to hide, but his paws had

an enormous spread and he used them with great effec-
tiveness.

The reindeer slowly moved down Big Stream Valley, followed by the bears. Quite a few reindeer were
left lying in Toivo's path. Ramti followed him and ate
his fill. It was real gluttony for him, and such occasions
were also feast days for hawks, foxes, and other beasts
of prey.

But in time the mushrooms began to wilt and fall
from their stems, and the leaves lost their color, dried
up and floated away. The mushroom season was over
and the reindeer returned to the mountains. The bears
followed them as far as the timberline, where they
found a lot of crowberries, whortleberries, blueberries
and lingonberries. They tasted good as a change from
the meat diet.

The long absence from human beings had caused
their fear of them to diminish somewhat. Still, when
they wanted to sleep, they would seek out a well-pro-
tected thicket. But they wandered fearlessly back and
forth above the timberline, where their dark bodies
could be seen from far off. After the prodigal life they
had been living, they would have done better to hide
than to call attention to themselves. But they felt too
carefree to think about that.

One night Sjur and a mountain hunter came walking up the valley. Sjur had found the dead reindeer and had gone down to the village to fetch the best marksman in the region. This was going to be a real bear hunt!

Oblivious of danger, the bears were as usual busy eating berries. Sjur and the hunter saw them from a distance. Quickly they made plans as to how to proceed. This was the perfect opportunity. Both of them were well armed and neither of them was afraid to confront even the big bear at close range.

Their plan set, they slowly crept toward the bears. Both of them would, if possible, fire the first shot at the big bear because he looked as if he would be difficult to fell. And then—well, they would have to play it by ear.

The sun was sinking and a cool wind swept across the moor. The big bear was grazing near the timberline. His shadow looked like a large gray cloth spread out over the moor. Higher up, Ramti was strutting around, feeling very sure of himself.

The hunter and Sjur were coming through the underbrush below the timberline, slowly advancing from nine hundred to six hundred feet, and from six hundred to three hundred. They wanted to get still closer to be sure of their aim.

At that moment some hawks came flying along the timberline. They caught sight of the hunters and rose, fluttering and screeching loudly. Toivo looked up. He knew the warning cry of the hawks and became apprehensive. He felt he had better get away—at least into the sheltered underbrush.

The hunters were furious. Hawks! Those raucous creatures had warned the crafty old bear, and now he was running away. They took wild potshots at him, but not a single bullet touched him.

Toivo lumbered back down through Big Stream Valley's birch forests, now practically barren. From time to time he stopped and looked back, expecting to see Ramti. He was now used to having him around and liked his company.

Ramti fled from the valley, away from the shots and the hunters' voices. He climbed to the nearest mountain ridge and beyond it. Only then did he sit down for a while and wait for Toivo. But when he didn't come, Ramti took off with big leaps to escape the pungent smell of gunpowder which was pursuing him. Before the autumn night had enveloped everything in darkness, he was already almost a mile from Big Stream Valley. He kept on going even after dark. He was heading in the direction of Beaver Valley, which he remembered from the previous year.

The night was cool, the sky was filled with stars, and a round moon was rising beyond the horizon. For long stretches the moor was flat and free from obstacles. A

young, strong bear like Ramti could cover this terrain very swiftly.

An inquisitive blue fox was following him, and for a long time a mountain owl kept him company. Ramti was aware of their presence, but it didn't bother him. The fox was quiet, and the owl hovering above him didn't make a sound. Her globelike eyes reflected the moonlight and glittered greenish yellow. Sometimes they looked as if they were attached to a stone on which the owl was sitting. But if Ramti made a move toward those globes of light, they would again rise toward the sky and again swoop downward in an arc behind or in front of him.

At daybreak he came upon a stream full of salmon. They were spawning, and many of them had swum off into shallow waters. Ramti stopped and watched the fish try to get out of this trap into which they had gotten themselves. He decided to fish for just a little while, but after he had caught and eaten the first fish, his appetite kept him busy for the rest of the day. Before nightfall he had succeeded, unintentionally, in freeing almost every fish from the shallow water trap.

The following morning the stream was just as lively as the day before. New fish had come during the night and Ramti again had a busy day. It wasn't easy to catch fish with his paws. Slime and weeds got stuck in his claws and, when he finally had a fish firmly in his grasp, it would wriggle out and swim away. Sometimes the water got so muddy that he couldn't see the salmon. Then he would crawl up on the bank of the stream and shake his wet fur. After a while he would again catch a glimpse of a spotted salmon, and he would throw himself back into the stream with renewed energy. About every tenth effort was rewarded, and it seemed to be just the right proportion of fisherman's luck to hold Ramti's interest.

There were no berries at this altitude, not even a crowberry bush. There were only moss and a bit of lichen. Ramti nevertheless settled down at the stream for quite a while. Salmon was among the best things he had tasted thus far—fresh, cold, and succulent. All he had to do was wait, and these marvelous tidbits would appear night after night.

But at this high altitude autumn came early. One morning when Ramti awoke, both he and his surroundings were covered with snow. Ice was floating in the stream, and all the shallow parts were frozen. This was the end of his fishing. He tried his luck for a while, sloshing about in the stream so that water and ice splashed in wide circles around him, but he didn't catch a single fish. A fish head that he had rejected the day before was his breakfast.

Then, following his original plan, he continued in the direction of Beaver Valley.

8. Ramti's Autumn Expedition

AUTUMN was also making its mark in Beaver Valley. The ground was still bare below the timberline, but it was cold and dreary. Rain and fog dripped from naked willow and birch branches. The stream had a light green tinge from the ice formations among the stones at the bottom. The surrounding mountains were completely white.

Instinctively Ramti headed for the grazing lands which his mother had shown him the previous year. Then they had yielded much, but now they were bleak and empty. He stumbled around among rotten leaves and dead plants. The angelica plant and the mountain lettuce were brown and sour, and just as foul-tasting as they looked. Neither did the frozen berries tempt Ramti, who so recently had pampered his stomach with succulent salmon. He had to find another source of food.

On his way up the valley he looked for lemmings. At the top, where only a few wind-ravaged birches had managed to hold on, he came upon a reindeer that had just been clawed by a wolf. The wolves were still around, and only when Ramti showed his fiercest mien was he able to drive them away—or at least keep them at a distance while he was eating. Then he took a siesta on a large stone nearby. When he awoke, he tried to approach the reindeer with the same technique he had used before, but this time it didn't work. The wolves had gathered in a large pack, and they not only defended their prey, but chased Ramti down to the stream and across it.

After this defeat he quickly zigzagged down the valley. In this way he crossed his own tracks. He sniffed at them. They smelled good; there was still an aroma of fish about them. He sat down and contemplated the mountains from which he had come. He thought of the salmon stream, but he also remembered his laborious trudge through the snow after leaving it. The mountains had become even whiter. It was too late to go up there. Snowdrifts were whirling among the peaks and were even descending into the forest.

Ramti made his way along the banks of the stream. The storm was becoming more violent, and frisky gusts of wind played hide-and-seek on the waves, continuing through the valley and sweeping it clean of leaves. There was no sound except for the roaring of the storm.

The beavers had built a high dam across the narrow part of the stream, and on the bank they had constructed an enormous hut. Ramti had an urge to see what it looked like inside. This involved a lot of work. The beavers had built their hut of anything that happened to be around, which they had woven into walls several layers thick. Ramti scratched and tore away part of the debris; he classified some of it in piles, discarding the rest. Finally he fell into a hole—the beaver dwelling. But he still didn't know what it looked like. The door was under water and he had come in the wrong way.

Night plunged everything into darkness. Ramti was just about to settle down when he suddenly caught sight of something that lured him on—sparks of fire in the air. They were coming from the chimney of a small cabin nearby, through whose square windows Ramti saw the flickering light of the fire inside. He came up close to the cabin and walked around it. He heard the sound of muffled voices, and the smell of cooking came from a door which was slightly ajar. Ramti was both frightened and curious. He wanted very much to get at an elk shoulder that was hanging on the cabin wall. But then the door opened. A man came out and went to the stream for a bucket of water.

Ramti quietly padded back into the forest. He remembered his bad experiences with human beings. They were not to be trusted.

On the small path leading from the cabin he smelled shoe polish, man, and elk. He followed the scent and came to the place where an elk had been shot. There was a lot of meat left, and he quickly took care of it. Most of the meat was hanging from the birches. But in his opinion it had been put in the wrong place. He immediately began rearranging the larder. He dug a hole in the ground and put the meat in it. While he was working, he took a bite out of every piece, and if it happened to be a small one, he ate it all.

Toward morning he was full and content, but also tired. As usual, he went only a short distance from his food reserve to enjoy a well-needed rest.

But it didn't last long. Two hunters appeared and awakened Ramti with their loud voices and unpleasant-sounding words. He peered through the underbrush and saw the men examining the hole where he had put the meat. When they came toward him, he moved farther away so that he could rest in peace.

The following night he returned for another meal. It was still dark and stormy. His sense of smell assured him that no human beings were around. He was able to enjoy his meal undisturbed, and also during the two nights that followed.

But the next day the hunters came back. They were walking quietly. One of them was carrying a heavy object—a huge bear trap. The elk hunt had turned into a bear hunt.

Perspiring and out of breath, the men laid down their burdens. The bear trap was rusty and its large, scissor-like blades gaped menacingly. It had held many bears in its grip until the hunters arrived on the scene. Of the animals who had been caught in it, few had come through alive.

The men were moving quietly and talking in whispers. They put the trap near a large birch and secured it with a strong chain. Then they camouflaged it with a thin layer of moss and dry leaves and hung some large pieces of meat from the branches. Around the trap they spread smaller pieces of meat to tempt the bear. Now he would get what was coming to him! When darkness began to fall, they left as quietly as they had come.

The day had come to an end. The contours of Beaver Valley had been blotted out by darkness and a heavy snowfall. No moon and no northern lights brightened the night, which soon became as inky black as only an autumn night in the mountains can be.

Ramti again padded quietly toward his food supply. As he approached the elk remains, he stopped and sniffed. A fresh scent of man put him on his guard. For

safety's sake he walked around the hole. By sniffing at tracks he could tell that the two-legged creatures had left. Reassured, he went up to the meat, where the smell of elk, man, birds, and steel mingled in a single, unidentifiable odor.

As he had come here to eat, he didn't lose any time. By now he was used to other animals' moving the pieces he had hidden. When he didn't find food in his hiding place, he took what was lying around on the ground. He looked around and saw the big piece of meat hanging from the birch. He had to climb up to reach it, but that was no problem. By getting a firm grip with his claws, he hoisted himself up the tree trunk. He ripped off the meat, held it in his mouth for a while before letting it drop to the ground. Then it happened! The meat landed right in the middle of the trap, which slammed closed with a terrible noise. Terrified, Ramti lost his grip on the tree trunk and fell, but was instantly back on his feet. What were these clanking iron chains and sharp blades he was stepping on? Beside himself with fear, he leaped away on all fours, away from this crashing, clanking noise.

The rest of the night he spent on top of the hill where he had begun his lair. From there he had a good view, and through the night he kept a watchful eye in all directions. That terrible thing at the hole might come rattling tqward him.

At daybreak he spotted the hunters. They walked up to the trap, mumbled something about the "sly rascal" and then slowly followed his tracks, which was easy in the fresh snow.

While they were still at a considerable distance, Ramti began to make decisions. He didn't want to run up the valley, nor did he want to climb the mountain. The snow was too deep up there, even in the wooded areas. His only alternative was to skirt a long mountain chain and continue toward the spruce forest in Big Stream Valley, where he felt at home. He set off and was pursued day after day, mile after mile. He stopped every night, but when at daybreak he discovered that he was being followed, he had to push on. Down in Big Stream Forest he knew the terrain well and was therefore always able to travel the easiest path. He crossed the swamp where he had caught frogs as a cub, and the hill where he had bit off Toivo's tail. He also came past the place where he and his mother and Toivo had feasted on mutton a few years ago. He quickly traversed the path over which he once had been carried as a prisoner. Then he made a wide sweep, doubling back on his tracks to see if he was still being followed, and when he saw that this was so, he ran still farther down into the dense spruce forest.

But he didn't know this area very well and he walked and ran as best he could through the deep snow. The flight brought him farther and farther away from his native ground, where it was no longer possible for him to stay. A winter drowsiness had come over him and he would have preferred to lie down. But each time he stopped to find a suitable place, he would always hear the scraping of skis and the sound of human voices behind him.

The forest had been thinned out in places to make room for settlements. He saw large farms and small ones, ski tracks and sleigh roads. He met elks, who quickly got out of his way, and foxes, and all kinds of wild animals. He would also have encountered human beings if his sense of smell hadn't warned him that they were in the vicinity.

Finally he reached a large, half-frozen river. Sometimes walking on the ice, sometimes swimming, he followed the course of the river for a whole day and far into the night. Then he took a solidly frozen sleigh road which led into another pine forest. Here he was able to walk without leaving tracks. A dense pine grove grew close to a small stream. Ramti took a long leap toward it and kept on leaping from tree to tree. It was the first day in a long time that he hadn't been followed.

In the distance he heard dogs barking, but it didn't bother him. He also heard the tinkling of bells and the sound of cars. But they all came from a great distance.

He began to feel at home in this sheltered pine

forest, and he was even more pleased when he found a big ant hill under a dense pine that was still dry and warm. Out of this hill and pine branches, he made himself a temporary resting place, in which he soon fell asleep.

9. An Unusual Winter Dwelling

RAMTI had been sleeping for a couple of weeks when he was suddenly awakened by a shattering noise in the otherwise silent forest. Horses were trotting forth and back, pulling large sleighs behind them, and on the sleighs sat drivers, urging the animals on. The roads were being plowed; echoing through the forest were the sounds of axes and of sharp-toothed saws. Tree after tree went crashing to the ground. Some of the men came into the forest whistling merrily, others were grumbling, and a few trudged silently through the snowy forest.

When it got dark the noise stopped. Ramti decided to try and stay where he was. The morning brought with it the same commotion, but Ramti curled up in his ant hill. The dense pine protected him and he felt very pleased at being able to see but not be seen. After a few days he paid no attention whatsoever to the various noises which reached his ears.

Ramti happened to have constructed his lair where timber was being cut. Many trees bore a metal sign indicating that they were to be felled, cut into logs and transported to the watercourse. The forest was dense, and the trunks were massive. With the shortness of the days at this time of year, the work didn't progress rapidly. However, every day brought the lumbermen closer to the tree beneath which Ramti had installed himself.

His tree also bore a metal sign. An encounter with one of the lumbermen was therefore unavoidable if he didn't escape in time. But now he was used to the noise around him. Besides, he was drowsy and had no desire to go out and trudge around in the snow.

One afternoon the inevitable happened. A lumberman slowly approached Ramti's tree. It didn't look like an easy one to tackle; it was too scrubby and knotty. When the man struck a blow with his axe at the tree to see if it was in good condition, there was a hollow, jarring crash. Then Ramti thought things had gone far enough. Angry and frightened, he crawled out and stared through the pine branches at the robust man who was standing on the other side of the tree.

Their eyes met. Each most certainly thought the worst of the other. The pine was a barrier between

them; but each had the same instantaneous reaction. At the same instant Ramti and the lumberman began running as fast as they could in opposite directions.

All around Ramti were runaway horses and panicky men. There was an uproar the like of which he had never seen. Everyone was fleeing from Ramti, and he in turn was fleeing from them. Finally he reached the edge of the clearing, and ran panting along an old sleigh road which took him still farther away from the upheaval.

Another peaceful night descended on the forest.

But once again things looked bad for Ramti. Discouraged and miserable, he spent most of the night watching and listening. The snow lay three feet deep and the going was difficult, so he could advance only short stretches at a time. Besides, he felt very drowsy and tired. Often he would nod with sleep, and little wonder, for nature had meant him to sleep at this time of year—which he would have done if he had been left alone.

Now he was being followed by two lumbermen on skis. At dawn he heard them trying out their rifles before starting to follow the bear tracks. The morning was cold and clear, and the sharp rifle shots echoed through the icy blue air. Shortly thereafter, he heard the sound of ski poles and the scraping of skis along the road he had traveled. He plodded on ahead.

On the way he came upon a large herd of elk, who fled, terrified at the sight of him. Without having the slightest desire to pursue them, he followed their tracks, in which it was easier to run. He kept behind the elk and in this way managed to keep his pursuers at a distance until night came and interrupted the chase.

Then the elk and the bear stopped as well as the hunters. They were all exhausted and all slept soundly during the night, the elks on the ice of a small lake, Ramti under a large fallen tree, and the hunters in a cabin. The hunters were the first to stir, and they awakened Ramti. He in turn alerted the elks, and the fierce hunt resumed.

A new and violent snowstorm began. Ramti wasn't always able to hear his pursuers. Sometimes it seemed as if they had given up, but when he was about to settle down, he would catch a glimpse of their dark ski clothes through the trees. Again he had to move on. At one point he heard the sound of bullets behind him and one of them almost seared his fur. But again he got away.

Toward nightfall the elk ran out on a road, followed by Ramti. It reeked of oil and gasoline. But the way was smooth so he kept on running. Even when the elk jumped over the mounds of snow on the side of the

road and disappeared into the forest, he kept right on going along the road. Then it got dark. He met a car with bright headlights. The car stopped, honked noisily and kept flashing its lights. The brightness blinded Ramti and he sat down, confused. The next second he was again alone, surrounded by darkness. The car roared around a curve and was gone.

Ramti trudged on listlessly, mile after mile. He was surrounded by darkness and snow flurries. There wasn't much traffic at night, and he was just about the only traveler on the road. He had no idea where he was going. He was a stranger in strange surroundings.

It was the night before Christmas Eve. To Ramti, it was an ordinary, snowy winter night. The only thing unusual about it was that he was walking on a road for the first time. But there were more unusual things in store for him. . . .

A man had gone to the forest to cut down a Christmas tree. The darkness and the snowstorm had held him up, but he finally got to the road, put the Christmas tree on a sled and started toward home. His village was about a mile and a half away.

Ramti was already in the village, and under the protection of darkness, he looked at all the houses and lights with great astonishment.

There was a lighted Christmas tree at the crossroads,

and many windows were lit up by sparkling red stars. But all these lights disturbed him and he soon wandered off in the direction from which he had come.

It was then he met the man with the Christmas tree. He practically ran right into him—the darkness and the driving snow flurries were blinding. As most human beings do when they are taken by surprise, the man began to scream, and raised the sled as a defense against the terrifying bear.

Ramti turned right around and ran back toward the village. There he stopped, hesitating between the high embankments of snow on either side of the road until the man with the sled reappeared. He kept on calling for help while Ramti backed away from him foot by foot.

A dog appeared on the scene, followed by two men with torches, whose flickering lights were continually being snuffed out by the wind. The dog barked and Ramti growled. He countered the attacks of the men and the dog as best as he could. But the noise and confusion forced him off the road and out into the soft snow. He came onto a field and followed a path which led to a farmhouse where women were standing and screaming at open windows. The pursuers were joined by several men. But Ramti managed quite well. Bears were rarely seen this close to the village, and in the inky darkness none of the men dared get close enough to the bear to shoot him.

The dog proved to be the most troublesome until Ramti could get him alone and give him a good whack. His howls were dreadful, and to avoid the same fate, the hunters decided to stop and to interrupt the bear hunt until morning.

So Ramti went on without pursuers. The storm raged in the open spaces between the farms. The path was completely snowed under, and huge drifts were forming everywhere. Ramti panted with exertion and fury. He slid down a hill, reached a riverbank and struggled along through the snow.

Then he lost his footing. He kept on sinking until he landed in a deep cave. Suddenly all was still. Above him he heard the roaring of the storm. He had found peace and shelter and felt very much like staying. Never before had he been this exhausted.

But he spent a restless night. The experiences of the last few hours gave him no peace. He began pacing back and forth in the rectangular cave. Two sturdy poles at the edge of the river supported the roof, which was constructed of heavy beams; a stone ledge against the embankment held up the beams. The only way out was a hole straight ahead. But Ramti didn't want to go anywhere.

When the morning of Christmas Eve dawned, the snowstorm was just as impenetrable as it had been the day before. The news of the dangerous bear had spread from farm to farm, and the villagers were apprehensive. Many stayed indoors all day, and few ventured as far as the store. Only the most courageous went out to hunt the bear.

The snow had already obliterated Ramti's tracks, and no one would ever have believed that the wild beast from the forest was lying under the boat landing on the river. The hunters returned to their homes in the firm belief that the bear had fled to the forest. Now they were going to celebrate Christmas before they continued the hunt.

So Ramti was left undisturbed. He began to feel very much at home where he was. Snowdrifts covered the boat landing and no fierce winds could get through to him. Against the abutment he made himself a comfortable bed, and from it he had a clear view of the river and the part of the village which was situated on the other side. But no one could see him.

From this sheltered spot he listened to the muffled sounds of the church bells early on Christmas morning. He saw sleighs leave the farms and cross the icy river. Every sleigh had tinkling bells and flaming torches. They came close to the landing, disappeared in the direction of the village, stopped at the church, and after an hour drove back the same way. Horses were neighing and children were laughing and singing.

But after that all was quiet once more. Ramti finally settled down to sleep and his long-needed winter rest.

10. The Journey Home

WINTER passed slowly. For the most part, Ramti slept soundly under the boat landing, but sometimes he would awake with a jolt. There were many children in the village. Most of them went to school weekdays, but during their free time they would slide and toboggan down the hills toward the river. One day they even came flying out on the landing, which they used as a running jump. That day they shrieked and laughed more than usual.

Soon afterward they cleared the ice right outside the landing for an ice-hockey field. During the next few weeks they spent every evening there, practicing, batting balls around, shouting, quarreling, and laughing. Everything they did was equally disturbing to Ramti. He tried to shut his eyes and sleep, but he couldn't really settle down to rest anymore.

Worst of all was the Sunday when an ice-hockey team

from another village came to play against the local team. This brought a crowd of spectators to the landing. Some of them even sat down, dangling their feet over the edge. The hockey game didn't last too long, but Ramti thought it would never end. Sometimes he would let out a muffled growl at the dangling legs. But no one heard him amidst the shouting.

After that Sunday, things calmed down around the landing. The ice-hockey field was melting away, and ski conditions deteriorated every day. The young people began to plan for summer sports and betook themselves elsewhere. Now Ramti had peace once more, and while he was sleeping, gentle winds removed the snow from the forest. Water from the glaciers began to run down the hills and the bare spots became larger and larger. But Ramti was oblivious to what was happening outside.

One day he was again awakened by noise and laughter, this time by a gang of boys who were clomping along the landing. The boards were now free from snow. The spring sunshine had dried and shrunk the lumber so that big cracks had formed between the boards. Every step the boys took, especially when they ran, were like hammer blows on Ramti's head. The mounds of snow on either side of the landing had also been melted down by the sun so that daylight was seeping into his quarters.

He looked around, wide awake and apprehensive. Below the tip of the landing was a hole in the ice, large enough to accommodate several fishing lines. The boys were baiting their hooks with worms and sinking their lines into the hole. Then they lay down on their stomachs and moved their fishing rods up and down. A couple of them had colorful flies, which lay bobbing up and down on the surface. Sometimes a fly would be pulled down under the water; then would come a shriek from one of the boys who had a flapping perch on his line. The small fish would then be thrown under the landing while the larger ones landed in a knapsack.

The perch fishing went on until the boys' mothers called in loud voices that it was time for lunch. As the boys scrambled back across the landing there was more thumping over Ramti's head. Fortunately, it didn't last long.

Minutes later, a flock of crows appeared and greedily devoured the remains of the fish. Their screeching stirred Ramti's fighting spirit and the smell of fish aroused his appetite. He crawled out a few feet and snorted at the crows, who dispersed, croaking and flapping their wings. They didn't return, but instead settled in some trees near the village, where they screeched their indignation at having been driven away from the landing. They kept complaining far into the night.

It was a pale, cool night, filled with signs of spring.

Ramti went up to the hole in the ice and drank. He then gathered the small discarded perch and ate every one. He even cleaned out the worm can that the crows had knocked off the landing.

Cautiously he crawled up the riverbank to have a look around. From a creek farther down came the pungent smell of oil from a sawmill. Black smoke belched skyward, and since Ramti didn't like either the smell or the noise, he set out in the opposite direction.

When he left the landing, the village was sleeping. The snow had become soft and mushy, and his huge tracks betrayed the direction which he had taken. He followed the riverbank until he reached a waterfall. He jumped from stone to stone past the rushing water and crossed the river above the falls. Then he climbed a mountain, the southern slope of which was free from snow, where he found some grassy patches which still had a few watery berries from the previous year. There he settled for a while because he also discovered an ant hill with thousands of delicious ant eggs. After his long fast, they tasted especially good to Ramti.

By the time he left the mountain, the cold night air had caused a hard crust to form on the snow. He longed to get up into the mountains, but the way was long and difficult. He alternated between long strides and trotting, and sometimes even took off at a wild gallop.

The snow was crunchy; he was able to get a good grip with his claws, which increased his speed.

The next day he came to a new mountain, which had more patches of bare ground, berry bushes and ant hills. It seemed a perfect place to make a rest stop. He took a bath in a spring, ate and slept, and had the extra good fortune to find a dead crane beside a bog, which he thoroughly enjoyed. By the time he had plucked and eaten it, another cold night had made a hard, solid crust for him to travel on. By now he was in very good spirits, and during the night he covered a great distance.

Ramti had adopted the habits of male bears, who move restlessly around during the spring months, traveling at night and resting during the day. The only difference was that Ramti was set on reaching higher altitudes. Each night brought him closer to his home ground, from which he had been driven mile after mile during the previous fall and winter. One morning, from the top of a mountain, he saw Big Stream Valley, and then he knew he was almost home.

But he had reached the mountain highlands ahead of spring, and for the past few days it had become a problem to find something to eat. There was always a small parade of lemmings, but that diet was meager for a bear. The small beasts had an uncanny ability to slip away, especially if the snow collapsed under Ramti.

Ramti decided to stay in the pine forest—at least for the time being. Not far away a reindeer cow had died of old age, and the hawks were quick to indicate the spot. A number of animals had already gathered there, and more kept coming. In the beginning Ramti was greedy. But when he had had his fill of reindeer meat a few times, he became more generous. He left the carcass to the other animals now and then to escape the turmoil.

One day he had a visit from one of his own kind— Toivo. But how old and scrawny the bear had grown! And he was snappy and ill-tempered besides. As if the reindeer were his own prey, he chased hawks, crows, magpies, foxes and every other living thing away from the spot. Heaven help the one who happened to come near him! He was even nasty to Ramti, who was now well fed, at peace with the world, and not interested in quarreling. To get away, he began the last lap of his journey to Big Stream Valley in dense fog and rain. But he wasn't keeping his usual pace. He would amble about here and there, visiting places filled with memories for him. He tore up roots, looked for larvae, and made a long detour to the grazing fields near the village. Then he was ready for the last lap of his trip.

On a beautiful spring morning, he found himself

standing in front of his childhood home in Big Stream
Valley. Two new bears had been born there during
the winter, of another female bear. The female had
gone on an expedition and the cubs were playing outside the lair. Ramti had a quick look around his old

home and then he settled down on the ledge outside. Although he was now a mature bear, he was still young, and when the little ones wanted to play, he was happy to stay.

The mother bear appeared carrying a dead crane in her mouth. She became frantic at the sight of Ramti. When she snarled at him, he moved aside without a grumble. But he settled down not far from the lair to observe this family. The female bear suckled the cubs and then pushed them into the lair. Placing herself so that her body covered the entrance, she greedily devoured the crane.

Ramti lingered around his childhood home all day. But when the female bear indicated that she wanted to be alone with her cubs, he quietly slipped down the cliff. In the steepest places he used his claws as a brake, but the rest of the way, he scrambled down as best as he could. When he glanced upward, the female bear and her cubs were only tiny dots up on the plateau.

The inlets of Big Stream were still frozen so Ramti had an easy time climbing up the valley. He had spent so much time down in the forest that he was very eager to see the mountains again, although he did stop from time to time. At the point where Big Stream crossed the glen through which he was traveling, Ramti ran into an otter. The otter was fishing and seemed to be doing very well. Beneath the flat rock where he lived, he had laid in a fine stock of speckled salmon, but unfortunately he was not able to defend his property. The skirmish between him and Ramti was a short one. It ended with the otter's throwing himself into the water and swimming away, while Ramti ripped away the stone and devoured every fish.

That meal reminded him of his own fishing experience in the mountain stream the previous autumn. Once his thoughts had gone in that direction, his legs weren't slow to follow.

Ramti kept mostly to the highest ridges, which had been swept free of snow, and after a day and a night he reached his destination.

But the fishing spot he remembered with such pleasure was still entirely covered with ice and snow. He lay around the stream for a couple of days, but the situation didn't change. Rivulets began to trickle down small furrows, but they were mostly formed by pelting rain which came out of rapidly moving gray clouds. It seemed pointless to stay.

In heavy rain and fog Ramti continued to wander. He couldn't see more than a few feet ahead of him and had to stick to the banks of the stream. This brought him to a big lake, also covered with ice, and he continued aimlessly. Suddenly he stumbled on a hole in the ice; he couldn't believe his eyes. There lay

a large, splendid, fresh trout. Ramti's mouth watered; he was overjoyed. Then he looked around and sniffed. If there was a fish on the ice, there could also conceivably be a . . .

From a distance he heard a faint grinding sound. He was curious and walked in the direction of the noise. He wasn't able to see a thing, but the noise continued so it was easy for him to locate it.

Ramti found himself right behind a fisherman who was drilling a hole in the ice. At that instant the man finished, picked up his drill and turned around to look for his fishing tackle.

He saw the bear. They were both equally terrified and both raced off in opposite directions.

Ramti now headed across the mountain. He wandered along the bleak plateaus, but had lost all sense of direction. Then he saw a huge, dark object far up on the summit. It looked like a bear standing on two legs, but it could also be a big, fat human being. To be on the safe side, he made a circle around it, hoping to find out what it was.

It didn't give off any smell, and Ramti kept on closing in on it. At last he found himself next to a cairn which was used as a landmark to designate the Swedish-Norwegian border. He lifted his leg on the strange object and then lay down beside it and fell asleep.

When he awoke the sky was bright blue. Two shrill

mountain geese were chattering above him. He yawned. The sun was high and the ground seemed to be seething with life. At a distance he saw the edge of a birch forest—it was the upper part of Big Stream Valley—and that was where he was heading.

Far in the distance Sjur was standing on a peak, looking around with his spy glasses. Despite his aversion to bears, he had to admit that the large, handsome bear making his way up Big Stream Valley was an impressive specimen.

11. Spring Sojourn
in Big Stream Valley

RAMTI came from the mountains to the north, and up there the snow still lay solid and many feet deep. But when he came into Big Stream Valley, he kept sinking into soft snowdrifts. At the bottom of the valley he hardly made any progress at all. He plunged into snow up to his belly, got furious and struggled, unable to get a foothold. He was too heavy, and no matter how he gripped with his claws, the snow refused to carry him.

In discouragement he lay down on his belly, rested and looked around. Both sides of the valley were still covered with snow, but at the eastern end of Big Stream Valley he was able to discern a knotty, brushy forest with bare spots. One of them stood out as being particularly big, and that is where he headed. He ran along a long, smooth range which was parallel to the mountain and Big Stream. Because it was exposed to the wind, the snow there never lasted long, and the sun had melted large patches of ground on either side.

Ramti got up on his hind legs and scratched his chest with one of his front paws. He had reached the edge of the forest, but he still had quite a distance to travel before he reached the bare spots on the other ridge. Standing up he was able to see beyond the trees. He got a new foothold and took another leap forward. With that he reached a steep slope, lay down and went sliding down it like an otter. He had to keep his eyes closed to protect himself from all the thorny branches that scratched his face. In this way, he ran into a huge tree stump. He lost his balance and made a half somer-sault, landing right in the middle of a snowdrift. His snout was in the snow and his legs were in the air. With strength—and an enormous amount of will power—he was able to maneuver himself into a normal position. But it took him quite a while to gain his true equilibrium. He sat there for some time, wet, di-sheveled, trying to dry himself. It was really difficult to get through the snow at this time of year.

When he finally raised himself, his broad backside had formed a huge, round hollow in the snow. He looked around and saw the stump. He crushed it, found some larvae and, with what was left of the stump, as well as some birch bark and dry sticks, made himself a bed in the hollow. While he was busy with that, the sun disappeared and a calm evening suffused with pale twilight settled around him.

The stillness was soon broken by the resounding laughter of white grouse in a nearby birch grove. The gay chatter spread to other trees and finally ended in a violent fight between two roosters at the edge of a bog quite close to Ramti. The whole area resounded with their spring frolic, and even Ramti began to listen. But the animated grouse conversation, the merry capers and the flapping of wings were not only an expression of gaiety. Quarreling during the mating game was part of it. The disputes were violent but didn't last long. The grouse had no time for drawn-out feuds. The roosters soon flew away, and Ramti followed them with his eyes as they winged their way across the blue-white snow and disappeared into the twilight. Then he again began fussing with the stump.

When he had finished, all that remained were some splinters. The rest had been crushed and trampled down into the snow, leaving a deep, comfortable hole. Ramti looked into it, nodded, yawned, and felt very sleepy. With his claws and teeth he gathered together a little more bedding from the materials around him— birch branches and underbrush. It turned out to be an excellent mattress, and of course he already had his long, gray-brown fur as a cover. It wasn't long before he was curled up on his bed, his snout between his paws.

The huge bare area which was his goal had been temporarily forgotten, but from time to time his shaggy legs would twitch. Although he was sound asleep, he sometimes spread his claws and curled his paws as if he were walking. He was sleeping and dreaming, and hearing the chattering grouse, though they were far, far away.

When he awoke, massive clouds were sweeping across the sun, while strong gusts of wind whirled sleet around. It stuck in the branches and in Ramti's fur, where it melted and dripped. He would have slept around the clock once more, except for this foul weather which had awakened him. Water was trickling into one of his ears—a most unpleasant sensation. He jumped up, rubbed his ear, shook his head and the rest of his body so that the water sprayed around him like mist.

Then he tried the snow again, but it hadn't improved one bit. After taking a couple of strides, he returned to his bed. For a while he sat hunched up, trying to protect himself against the wind, but he couldn't settle down. He scratched around in his wet bed, which was getting wetter by the minute. The previous day a small rivulet had taken the same path down the hill as Ramti. He looked uphill at the growing cascade of water, then turned his head and peered through the mist toward the valley with that huge bare spot. The sight of it quickly got him back on his feet.

Slowly he floundered through the wet snow, sometimes taking long strides and sometimes forging ahead with what seemed more like swimming strokes than anything else. He wasn't making fast progress, but then there was no reason to hurry.

The grouse were still trying to keep up their spring frolic, but the weather dampened their efforts. The storm often caught them in flight and dragged them down toward the ground. Their mating calls were muffled by the wind and the increasing surge of water coming down Big Stream.

When Ramti reached Big Stream there was just as much water running over the ice as under it. Ice floes were hurled up on the banks, while the water thundered on. Ramti sat watching this tumult for a while until a large ice floe came along, caught in two other floes and formed a bridge for him—or so he thought. But when he jumped on it, it broke loose under his weight and careened down the stream.

Ramti was terrified. He wasn't much of a sailor, and rapids especially put him into a panic. He desperately tried to keep on the ice floe, although he was flung back and forth like a rider on a wild horse. But he soon found himself overboard. Luckily he was catapulted toward the bank. An old, bent birch extended out over the stream. He got a grip on it and reached shore safely. From there he climbed as quickly as he could to the stretch of bare ground that had been taunting him for so long. But it didn't turn out to be so big as it looked, as Ramti discovered when he dug his claws into it and began wandering around. After a mere three hundred feet he ran into a steep precipice and, as he continued to walk, he found himself at the snow-bordered edge. But after the first round he realized that the bare plateau was better than nothing. Many lemmings were scuttling around his feet. He grabbed a few of them as he kept exploring the plateau. For a young bear it was a pleasure to walk on solid ground again, especially as bare patches were a rarity at this time of year.

Toward morning he had a strong urge to hunt, chiefly for sport, but also to fill his stomach. Lemmings and field mice had to flee for their lives into their underground runs or tight crevices. Nevertheless many of them ended up between Ramti's claws. He chewed, swallowed, licked his lips and looked around for something more substantial. He made several quick forays which sometimes yielded game. But the pursuit of small rodents was just profitable enough to keep him interested. When evening came he had had enough and sought shelter behind a big stone.

He was awakened by two cranes who had settled on the snowbank and were jabbering away. At the first shrill sound Ramti jumped up and began to run, but he soon realized that he was in no danger. The cranes were obviously communicating with other cranes down in the valley, and when they didn't stop, he became impatient. There had to be an end to this racket! If these long-legged noisemakers had come here to disturb the peace, they would just have to move. He didn't even have to begin to get nasty before they took off with languid movements and settled on a small spring near a bog. They were still too close, but for the time being, Ramti couldn't be bothered to chase them.

Instead he set out on a new tour of inspection, and all at once he became very busy on his new domain. At first there had been only a few lemmings, but like most other animals they preferred bare ground to snow, and many more had arrived while Ramti was sleeping. On the ridge closest to the stream, a flock of plovers were tuning up. They were the first of their kind to arrive, and they were now probably trying to entice more of their relatives to join them. The ridge was surrounded by crowberry bushes and the watery berries left from the previous year seemed to please these visitors from afar. But Ramti was by no means a generous host. As long as he was master of this plateau, it was risky for all smaller creatures to remain.

So the plovers and the cranes decided to move on.

Ramti watched them settle on a little strip of bare ground farther on. Then he decided to take a look around. It was still raining but the wind had died down, and although dusk had fallen, the visibility was good. In a short time the valley had completely changed. There were bare spots everywhere, and new rivulets seemed to form every day to carry the water down the mountain. But the biggest change had taken place in the stream. The ice had partially broken up, but in a small cove surrounded by stones, a small dam of ice and snow had formed, and above it, part of the valley lay like an oblong lake. Many trees were below the water line, and it confused the grouse, who didn't know where to play. Now their favorite groves were being visited mostly by geese and other migratory birds with webbed feet.

Spring had arrived a bit late, but it was making up for lost time. Throughout the night there was warbling and whistling and piping of thousands of migratory birds, and the following day there would be even more new voices in the valley. But many would continue their journey when night came, as almost all species traveled by night. Some would stay on and look for a mate, improving old nests or building new ones. White grouse and other migrants would have company for some time to come.

Unfortunately, a couple of peregrine falcons had turned up. They had already taken their first grouse and were plucking it high in their nest on a rocky ledge.

For the moment all living things had to tolerate Ramti's presence. Now and then he would venture forth to measure the depth of the snow with his legs, but when he found it too deep, he would return to the bare ground. Besides, he was in no hurry. He was really quite content with this spring sojourn.

12. A Stormy Spring Voyage

On THE evening after an exceptionally warm and sunny day, the dam in the stream burst with a terrible roar. At that moment Ramti was busy picking berries, but out of curiosity he stopped and went out on the ridge over the stream. Close to him water, snow, and ice came rushing by with a roar. The ground trembled under his feet when the wet mass forced its way with tremendous speed through the narrow canyon between the ridge and the slope opposite. Roots, earth, stones, everything in the way of the tremendous mass was swept along. As it came plunging down the valley it looked like an enormous, slimy, shapeless animal.

At the head of the valley the water level began to sink quickly. Hills that had been submerged for the past week or had protruded like small islands were quickly uncovered, and with them bogs and willows. Finally the marshy banks were exposed, to the unfet-

tered joy of a large flock of geese who saw the rich
grazing land from above. Although they all saw the
same thing at the same time, they had a desperate urge
to communicate. Suddenly there was disorder in the V
formation they had kept during their flight from the
south. They flew in all directions, circling downward,
and during the last stretch it looked as if they were having a race. The sky was filled with them, and they
seemed to collide in the air and land doing somersaults.
But all of them alighted gracefully, with earsplitting
cackles. Roots of horsetail and sedge which they found
on the banks soon silenced their cries.

The flood even reached the slopes and washed them
free from snow, old leaves and wilted plants. The flood
also brought trash of all kinds, which, as the water
receded, eventually sank to the bottom after whirling
around in the backwater under the waterfalls. But
many objects floated for a long time before they either
sank or were washed ashore. That was the fate of the
carcass of a dead reindeer which had thawed somewhere up in the valley, swelled to a huge size and, now
reeking, floated wherever Big Stream carried him.

The wind brought the smell of the reindeer to
Ramti. He sniffed the air and decided that the gamy
odor must be coming from the river. He set off immediately. Lemmings, field mice, berries—all were for-

gotten. Judging by the smell, there was more solid food
around. He went bounding down to the stream and
then followed the bank. The carcass had struck the
shoreline in a few places and left new scent as well as
tufts of hair. He jumped over streams, crossed spongy
bogs, and forced his way through thick underbrush. The
scent of a good repast was continually with him, but all
he got of it was the scent. Ramti had been rested when
he began running. But after trying to keep up with the
carcass floating down the river and tumbling over
numerous waterfalls, he began to feel a bit winded. He
panted, his tongue hanging far outside one corner of
his mouth. His fur became heavy with mud, sweat, and
slime. His legs ached so that he had to slow down to a
walk.

Night came, an inky-black one. On one side of him
the grayish-brown water flowed by, still muddy from
the sudden inundation. On his other side was the recently flooded ground, which widened as the valley descended. He saw sand snipes, ruffs, gulls, and many
other wading birds who spent the night motionless and
dozing. But when Ramti appeared, they all vanished,
flying ahead, settling, but then moving on again. For a
while he was joined by an otter, perhaps an old acquaintance. The otter came swimming along with the
current, dived, splashed around, perched on stones, but

soon left Ramti behind. He was extremely lively but then he, too, was a creature of the night. He was particularly lucky in getting a ride down Big Stream, whose water had never before flowed so rapidly. Perhaps he wasn't going anywhere but was only amusing himself.

At last the carcass stopped. It lay circling around the backwater current of a waterfall. When Ramti reached the spot, the reindeer was on its way upstream. He crouched in a thicket, dug his claws into the bank and waited for the reindeer to come close enough so that he could reach it with a leap. But the spongy carcass floated just far enough from the shore to make it impossible for Ramti to reach. Never had he wanted anything so much!

The reindeer floated out into the current and was carried swiftly along. Ramti leaped after it, which turned out to be unnecessary, as it was again drawn upstream by the current. All night the reindeer kept on playing games with Ramti. He walked and ran up and down the bank until he had made a real path. His eyes never left the reindeer. He was filled with rage and frustration and sometimes tried to hide in the hope that the reindeer would then come ashore. But the carcass followed the current, which in turn was governed by the laws of nature. The current sucked it into whirlpools in the same way it did roots and fallen trees. Laws

of nature apply to all, but of course Ramti wasn't able to grasp that. He probably thought that the reindeer was alive, as it was constantly in motion.

When the sun rose above the cliff which jutted out over Big Stream, and its rays began to burn Ramti's back, his movements became more languid. He sat down in a thicket and began to chew on some willow buds, which at least helped to appease his hunger. For dessert, he ripped up and ate some grass roots. Then he lay down with his head between his paws, staring at the stream until he was overcome by sleep. But even in deep sleep, he kept turning his head in the same rhythm as the whirlpool under the waterfall where the reindeer was whirling around.

Toward evening he was awakened by the furious barking of dogs, the shouting of people and the sound of reindeer bells. The noise came from the other side of the valley; some Lapps were herding reindeer up on the summit. The gray, furry mass soon disappeared over the ridge, and then the sound of men and dogs subsided.

Ramti looked up and his gaze stopped at the point on the cliff where he had lived as a cub. But the distance was too great to discern the entrance to his old cave. The cliff was now completely free of snow and the gray spots were beginning to turn green. As usual, the buzzards were out making their nightly rounds among the cliffs.

But the reindeer—what had happened to him? Ramti was instantly on his feet. The river had undergone such a drastic change that he hardly knew where he was. The water had receded and headlands, creeks, and stones had reappeared, and the whirlpool had subsided into a small, slowly rotating circle.

The smell of the carcass nevertheless assured Ramti that it wasn't far away, and it didn't take him long to locate it. It had gotten caught in a large root at the point where the whirlpool turned against the main current, and as the water was receding still, it was now lying quite a bit above the waterline. All Ramti had to do was to take the reindeer by the horns and drag it up to a place where he could have a private feast.

The days passed. The last birds flew by, or made a brief stop in Big Stream Valley. The sun opened the buds on the trees, and the valley was suddenly green. When the leaves had grown to the size of a mouse's ear, the nocturnal mating calls of the grouse ceased. The hens had laid their eggs and were sitting on them, so there was no further point to the roosters' enticing love calls.

But still, things were far from quiet for Ramti. There were lots of thrushes around who always seemed to have a reason for jabbering. There was sometimes a fox in the underbrush, or an ermine or a weasel, not to speak of the buzzards or sparrow hawks who came whizzing through the forest. The noise was terrible, whether the birds caught their prey or not.

In the hills and in the underbrush there were also other species of birds whose voices did not carry, but which were generally more appealing. As neighbors, Ramti had a couple of flycatchers who had built their nest in a willow tree. Next to them were a pair of willow warblers. Dippers flew up and down along the stream and even snipes drilled from time to time. They seemed to have established themselves on a bog beyond the hill.

But Ramti had stopped playing landlord. He was no longer interested in the small creatures, though the hawks still bothered him. The reindeer was his, and he had put it in a dense thicket, where he spent most of his time. It was only when he needed a bit of rest that he removed himself to a dry hill close by. But no sooner did he shut his eyes than he heard a hawk come screeching and attracting others to the carcass. Sometimes there would be such a racket that it was impossible for Ramti to sleep, either day or night. Sometimes he lost his temper and ran into the bushes growling furiously. The hawks, alarmed, would flutter away, but in an hour or so they would be back, clucking and screeching. When it became too much for him, Ramti decided to bury what was left of the reindeer in a bog and cover it with moss. That helped somewhat, but the hawks still hovered around with tufts of reindeer hair in their beaks, quarreling over the remaining scraps of meat.

In time Ramti tired of his inactive life. He rolled around, stretched his legs, flexed his muscles, pulled down a few saplings and played with them. He was healthy and well nourished and bursting with energy. It was spring, and nature was exhorting him to find a mate. His loafing did nothing to perpetuate the bear species.

He began wandering around in the forest, biting into tree trunks and leaving his saliva and scent behind. He would often lift his leg and spatter a tree trunk. If a female bear happened to cross his tracks, she would be easily able to smell him. This simple, direct behavior was pure instinct. Finally, after having looked for a long time, he detected the scent of one of his own kind. He sniffed the wind, took longer strides, and soon came upon a young female bear who was fishing for frogs in a stream. She was skinny and had long hair, but she had a friendly disposition, and in Ramti's opinion she was beautiful. He sniffed at her fur and she sniffed at his. With this they were ready to become a couple. As yet she wasn't ready for the mating game, but nevertheless indicated to Ramti that he pleased her.

The frog fishing didn't yield much; the frogs spent most of their time in the deep mud croaking. Since Ramti hadn't had anything to eat in several days, he began to feel hungry. This, coupled with his desire to take his mate to a better feeding place, made him go back to the buried reindeer. Sometimes she hesitated and didn't seem to want to go on. But when Ramti walked away from her and sat down to wait, she would always come plodding along in his tracks. After a long trudge he finally had the chance to show her what he had hidden. The carcass had shrunk considerably since he had first found it, but at least there was enough meat and bones left for a very good meal.

While the two were having a fine time gorging themselves, Toivo showed up. He sniffed at the female bear and, realizing what the situation was, became fierce and jealous. Ramti, who considered both the female and the reindeer his personal property, felt the same way. After all, he had pursued the reindeer for many miles down the river and had found the female and brought her to this feeding place.

The two males refrained from open conflict, but kept on eyeing each other with suspicion. Neither of them wished to remember that they had been friends in the past.

The female bear kept getting close to one of them, and then the other one was offended. A fight finally became inevitable.

It happened when Ramti had fallen asleep, and the female bear had lain down near him. Toivo became so furious that he whacked Ramti across the head with his paw. Half blinded by the blow and enraged, Ramti flew up, ready to sink his teeth into his adversary. But he miscalculated the distance and received a new blow, which felled him. He roared with rage and pain, and Toivo also roared. One of Ramti's eyebrows was ripped; blood was running into his eyes and along his muzzle. He saw Toivo through a mist of blood and heedlessly sprang at him. Toivo fell backward, and for a moment Ramti had the upper hand. But he couldn't see very well, and before he had gotten a good grip on Toivo, he was again struck to the ground.

The loss of blood made him weak, and as soon as he had a chance he ran away. He dunked his head in a nearby stream and let the cool water wash over his wounds. For a long time he waited for the female bear to join him, but she didn't appear. Downhearted, he lumbered on. The old fighter had won. Ramti had no intention of going back to continue the fight. He still had a certain respect for older bears.

Instead, he headed toward the mountains in the hope of finding a more loyal female. As he crossed the forest, true to his habit, he bit into a tree here and there to mark his path, just in case. When he reached the mountains, he went to every place that used to be frequented by bears, but he didn't run into anyone. There was the possibility that he might run into a female farther along Big Stream Valley. But then again, he had been there earlier in the spring and he didn't feel like going back. Instead, he decided to go in a westerly direction and ambled along ridges, mile after mile. Once he passed a large cairn which bore a number. The bears used to visit such boundary markers, but there was no scent of them anywhere.

For a while he nosed around the cemented pile of rocks, the result of man's work. At least it held his weight when he climbed up on it. Then he crossed the border at a brisk pace and found himself in Norway.

13. The Emigrant

RAMTI passed over a ridge and found himself in a new valley—Steep Valley, which merited its name. At the bottom, Steep Stream foamed and plunged, forming many cascades. The valley descended sharply toward the west, and to Ramti it seemed as if he were going down a dark, green cave. The dense forest became sparser in parts and the underbrush gave way to spruce copses.

After a week or so, Ramti's procreative instinct abated, and he became calmer. He had a good rest and he slowly began to orient himself in the glen he had discovered. Where the slopes weren't too steep, he found a lot of ant hills, which he thoroughly examined. The Norwegian ants were as good as the Swedish ones, as were the eggs. And the angelica and mountain lettuce, which were beginning to sprout in the valley, were just as succulent as in the other mountain valleys. Ramti quickly began to feel at home.

When he had reached the point where the valley spread out into fields, he began seeing houses and also people—and the animals that mountain farmers usually keep. In the summer, a whole community of farmers moved into the valley. Ramti sat on a ledge and observed life around the small, gray houses. He rarely went down there, and he never went to the places where children laughed and cried, women and men shouted and talked, cows mooed and horses whinnied. He left them alone. After all, he had the steepest part of the valley all to himself; neither human beings nor goats could get a foothold there. He didn't have to force himself on the villagers, and besides, they weren't even aware of his existence.

Once while Ramti was sleeping, another bear came and sniffed at his neck. Ramti woke up, yawned at the stranger and let out a muffled growl. Whether this meant "Welcome" or "Go away," the stranger had to decide for himself. At any rate, he stayed on with Ramti. After a while the two became such good friends that together they found and devoured the contents of an ant hill.

The stranger was about Ramti's size. His fur was golden brown, bleached by the sun; both he and Ramti

were shedding hair in masses. Ramti's new hair had
almost completely grown in around his temples and
his ears. The stranger's coat was a bit more straggly
than Ramti's, which indicated that he was older. Also,

his teeth and claws were more worn. But most of all, it was the gravelly voice which told his age.

At any rate, Arjo, Ramti's new friend, was familiar with the village of Steep Valley and its surroundings. And where Ramti had previously failed to find good paths, he now became thoroughly initiated. It soon became obvious that it was Ramti and not Arjo who was the stranger. All he had to do was to follow Arjo, who was a good climber and thoroughly familiar with the Norwegian terrain. He was also good at finding food. If the supply gave out in one place, he soon moved to another. Ramti devotedly followed his new friend, and as the mating season for bears was over, there was no reason to quarrel. Their diet consisted of many different kinds of grass and herbs, but there was also more substantial fare. Such delicacies as sheep and goats were sometimes available. This temptation induced the bears to draw closer to the village as the summer wore on. The scent of livestock was almost irresistible as it came wafting up the valley.

Finally one night, the bears took their first turn around the village. They could glimpse the houses between trees, and they heard cows mooing inside the sturdy timber walls. A horse was in a stable, stamping and gnawing at his manger. Another building smelled of sheep, and in a shed next to it a pig was slurping

his swill. There was no shortage of food—but unfortunately all the livestock were indoors. The only animal
outside was the dog, and he, in common with the rest
of his species, had an excellent sense of smell. He began
to bark furiously and ran forth and back tugging at his
clanking chain. A man came out and tried to quiet
him, and there was still more commotion. In the face
of all this, there was nothing for the bears to do but
retreat.

In the morning the women went around the houses
rattling their milk pails and other utensils, laughing
and talking. A while later the barnyard doors were
opened, and the livestock came out to pasture, mooing
and bleating, leaping around or standing motionless
and staring, until they were all pushed into an enclosure down at the river.

Not one of them strayed in the direction of Ramti
and Arjo. The grazing field was located in the worst
possible place from a bear's point of view. It was on a
peninsula which jutted out into the water—on one side
was Steep River and on the other, one of its tributaries.
It was impossible to get at the cattle without being
seen, especially as people were always bathing down at
the river or children were playing around on the sandy
banks.

The day passed with the usual tasks being performed
on the farm. Smoke and steam came from the house

where cheese was being made. Near a milk cellar was a butter churn. The woman who had been working it had moved out into the open, where she sat at her loom. Now and then she would wave a cloth around to keep the mosquitoes at a distance. Some of the men and women were busy with harvesting. Some people were visiting each other's cabins and drinking coffee, and others sat outside the front door or on the grass chatting. The children were down at the river or around the grazing field or swinging near the cabins. They seemed to be busy all day long.

Toward evening the cattle were brought back from the fields to the barnyard. Again there was the rattling of milk cans. Separators hummed monotonously. When they were through, the women rinsed the utensils in a stream, placed them upside down in a drying rack, hung up their smocks and disappeared into the cabins.

Farther up in the valley the bears lay listening and peering down at the people and animals through a screen of branches.

If they had been able to understand words and to follow events logically, they would have seen a dramatic incident. It happened when the animals were being herded home. A large goat with long horns took aim and with full force butted an old man in the back. After that he attacked a child. That was going too far! The goat was dragged by the horns to a small shed at the edge of the forest and put in solitary confinement. A man shut the door and placed a heavy bar outside. Such a capricious animal could not be allowed to wander about freely. It wasn't the first time that the goat had displayed his irascible temper.

When all was quiet in the village and the summer night enveloped the houses in a gray veil, the bears got up. That night they toured the village for the second time. Things were much calmer this time. The dog had been brought indoors so that he wouldn't cause a disturbance during the night. The bears approached the houses and went especially close to the shed where the goat was sitting under house arrest. They could hear him moving inside the timber walls, and the unmistakable odor of the goat seeped out of the cracks between the logs. The smell pursued them as they slowly made their way up the valley at dawn.

After a practically sleepless day, they slid down the mountain once more. That night they had a goal—the goat's shed. The August moon rose over the horizon, red and warm. A breeze gently stirred the leaves and a few woolly clouds slowly went sailing up Steep Valley, casting broad shadows. From time to time, the moon illuminated the timber walls of the houses and the forest which framed them, and also shed light on a crooked gulley with its surging water rushing down the valley. A perfect night for hunting!

They got the chance they had been waiting for. The bears made a few turns around the house nearest the forest, stopped, listened and sniffed. They circled around the goat's prison until they were right next to it. They stopped on the dark side, sniffing again. One thing led to another, and one of them began digging a hole. They both had an irresistible urge to see what the shed looked like from the inside, but most of all, they wanted to get at that goat. They took turns digging, and the one who was free would circle around the hut. The goat became aroused and ran up and down the mud floor inside.

All three of them became more agitated. The one who was digging scratched frantically, and splinters from the decayed beam and soil from under it flew in all directions. The one on watch ran around and around the hut as though on a merry-go-round. The whole hillside was thundering with activity.

Now the hole was deep enough so that they could look inside and see the goat. But in the diffused light he didn't look quite like himself. The moonlight streaming in through the cracks had changed his coat to yellow and black zebra stripes. But after Ramti and Arjo had taken turns peering through the hole, they both assured themselves that the shed still contained the object of their desire.

Suddenly something happened which caused the digging to cease abruptly. The one doing patrol duty hap-

pened to run into the beam which was leaning against
the door. It gave way and flew to one side with a crash.
The door opened on creaking hinges. When the goat in
that instant saw a shaggy bear head protrude from the
hole, he took a wild leap and landed outside. He was
now the prey of Ramti and Arjo. With no effort at all,
they dragged him into the forest and found that he
tasted as good as he smelled.

That morning the noise in the village was unusually
loud. And little wonder. The claw marks and the hole
the bears had dug were soon discovered. It didn't take
the men long to realize what had become of the goat.
There was a long, white trail of goat's hair leading
toward the forest.

The people's feelings toward the goat changed instantly. The day before, they had been up in arms
against him. Now they were filled with compassion,
despite the fact that the wicked goat had been destined
for slaughter. The poor thing—what a terrible fate.
Everyone remembered the goat as he had been most of
the time—an amenable animal, and most of all, a fine
breeding animal of pure race. He had even won a prize,
and his diploma had been framed and was now proudly
displayed in one of the cottages. That morning many
of the townspeople looked at it while their thoughts
turned to the terrible thing that had happened at the
edge of the clearing.

The killing had to be avenged. Rifles were taken out

of closets and loaded with the best available bullets. The dog was rewarded with an especially good meal. After saying good-bye, the hunters marched, grave and silent, into the forest, on legs that trembled just a little. But none of them showed any fear. The women and children stood lined up at the enclosure, waiting tensely. Behind the closed barnyard doors the livestock mooed and bleated, longing to be turned out to pasture. They couldn't understand why they had to stay indoors on just that day.

The hunters knew what they had to do and were determined to accomplish their mission. But how would they dare approach the strongest and most cunning of beasts in that dense forest? They discussed the problem in detail, making sure that no hunter would be taken by surprise and caught in a struggle with the bear—they did not know that there were two of them.

The forest seemed unusually dense and thorny to them. The beast could be lurking behind a spruce or crouching beneath its long, low branches. They had to stick close together and be on the alert; otherwise this expedition could end in catastrophe.

The bears heard the subdued conversation. They had already abandoned the goat and were moving away from the village. Scent from human beings filled the air and they heard branches cracking. In addition, much to their dismay, a dog was following in their tracks, barking loudly.

In the beginning they were able to drive the dog away, making it retreat. But when a shot was fired and a bullet came zooming through the air, they hesitated. When they retreated, the dog would once again pursue them. Then there was another discharge, this time from several rifles. The air was thick with the acrid smell of gunpowder. Suddenly a bullet dug a furrow in Ramti's forehead. His head pounded and, dazed, he sank to his knees, where he remained for several seconds. With a great effort, he managed to get up and reel away.

He was soon obstructed by the dog, who came at him and barked noisily, but the dog still backed away when Ramti went for him. For a while Ramti and the dog rolled around in fierce battle. Then they moved on to a spruce grove, where they pursued each other with ferocious intensity. Branches and moss were flying in all directions, and their wild cries echoed through the valley. The hunters stayed at a distance; none of them was in a particular hurry to approach the spruce grove. They had now seen not one, but two bears. One of them could attack at any moment.

But Arjo had slipped away. Since he knew the area well, he had escaped by running down into the valley and swimming across Steep River. Now he was sitting safely on the other side, listening to the uproar in the forest across from him. He was waiting for Ramti, but Ramti had other things to take care of, and Arjo had to wait in vain. The shooting, the smell of men and gunpowder had so thoroughly obliterated the scent of the bear tracks that neither of the bears would be able to reach the other one.

Ramti tried to determine in what direction Arjo had gone, but he was constantly bothered by the dog. When he stopped to drive it away, one of the hunters would come closer. Then he had to start running again. He leaped into a ravine and continued at the same pace until he reached a road at the foot of the valley. In this way he was able to throw both the hunters and the dog off the track. But he wasn't alone for long.

At a curve in the road he ran into a horse-drawn cart. The driver was on his way to the village to fetch butter and milk for the settlement below. The encounter lasted only a split second. The horse immediately shied away from the bear, bolted, and disappeared in a cloud of dust. Ramti disappeared just as quickly into the forest. Some troughs and buckets which had fallen off the cart in the violent turn were left lying on the road.

All of these events separated Ramti from Arjo and dispatched him in a different direction. Panting and sweating, he quenched his thirst in a spring. Since nothing seemed to be pursuing him, he risked stopping for a while. He heard the cart with the bolting horse rattling down the valley, so he didn't want to go in that direction. Up above, the events had been so shattering that he didn't want to return. He ended the day by creeping along the cliffs of Steep Valley. At dusk he turned off into a narrow glen that had been formed by one of Steep River's tributaries. A violent thunderstorm forced him into a crevice, where he sank down exhausted and fell asleep.

For a time Ramti wandered around aimlessly in the glen. There were no cabins and at least he was no bother to people and cattle. However, he bothered lemmings and ants. He also went through many beehives, for he was extremely fond of honey. But for the most part he lived on berries and plants.

Toward the end of summer he was as usual quite fat and also lazy. Slowly, he made his way back up the valley, and without being aware of it, he crossed the border and again became a Swedish subject. It meant nothing to him, because, wherever he went, he classified the area as his hunting ground. His instinct and memory were infallible. He was a bear from Big Stream Valley and he had to find his way home. He also had learned how to avoid danger. His strength alone was not always sufficient. He was obviously powerless against bullets and gunpowder. He kept on scratching the furrow that the Norwegian hunter's bullet had made in his head, and for a long time it gave him pain. Such things are hard to forget.

One evening he reached a small lake. Along the shore he found some tempting red cloudberries. They enticed him to walk around the points and inlets.

Suddenly he found himself in front of a rowboat which was turned upside down. He had been so absorbed in his berry picking that he hadn't noticed it. Startled, he was about to flee. But as the boat didn't move, it couldn't be dangerous. He went up to it and sniffed it from bow to stern. Then he became aware of an animated buzzing under the boat. It turned out to be two large wasp nests. Ramti well remembered the taste of their wax and their larvae from long ago, and he immediately poked his nose under the boat to tackle one of the nests. It didn't bother him in the least when the wasps attacked his shaggy coat. He was going to enjoy his meal!

But while he was having his feast, he caught sight of a man coming toward him along the lake shore. Ramti still had the second wasp nest to tackle. He hid in the bushes, hoping the man would keep on going.

The man, of course, had not the faintest notion that he was being observed by a bear. From his rucksack he pulled out some nets, which he was prepared to drop into the water. He started to turn the boat over

but quickly backed away. Never had he seen such a
mass of swarming, furious wasps. He couldn't possibly
get close to the boat.

He looked at the wasp nest from a respectful distance. How was he going to get rid of it? He had to
have the boat in order to put the nets into the water.
He would get stung to death if he tried to get near it,
and besides, he had a terrible fear of these flying beasts.

A rattlesnake to him seemed harmless, faced with this swarm. There were hundreds of them around the boat, all armed with stingers. While he was pondering his predicament, he had an idea. He would burn them! If he tore up a piece of dry birch bark, attached it to the end of a long pole, put a match to it and placed it under the nest, they would soon be routed out. The idea seemed workable, so he set about to execute it.

Armed with a torch, he patiently waited until most of the wasps had crawled out of the nest. Then he cautiously approached the boat. The bark was burning at the end of the pole. But as he held the flame down under the nest, he happened to be standing close to the other nest, which Ramti had demolished. Those wasps were maddened and attacked the man from all directions. He ran for all he was worth.

After the storm had passed, he saw to his horror that not only the wasp nest, but the whole boat had gone up in flames. The well-tarred wood had quickly caught fire. And what was much worse—the ground was burning. The forest was on fire! He ran around desperately, without being able to do anything about the blaze. Fortunately, the fire was restricted by the lake and the wet bog. But things were bad enough.

Ramti was quite puzzled by the commotion on the beach, especially when the flames started to spread and make their way toward the forest. Not knowing what to make of it, he ran higher and higher up the valley. But long after the sun had set and darkness had fallen, he continued to look back. He had seen northern lights before and also fire, but never before had he seen such red flames as down there in the valley. It wasn't easy for a bear to grasp what was happening on a still, dark, peaceful night such as this.

Toward morning, the fire subsided, but the whole valley was filled with a blue, reeking smoke. The smell made Ramti sneeze uninterruptedly, and he soon set out in the direction of Big Stream Valley.

14. Autumn in Bear Country

A NEW day dawned, tranquil but foggy. The dew was shimmering everywhere—in the vegetation, on the mountain moors, and in Ramti's glossy brown fur. For the moment he had decided to travel along the ridge, as this was the only place he could find his way during the early morning hours. It was still hard going, but slowly he covered a terrain shrouded by white fog.

When the sun began to rise he paused, settling himself like a statue on the highest peak. Here he had an unobstructed view, at first over quivering banks of mist which rose from the springs and bogs. Then the mist sank into the valleys and lowlands, and it looked almost as if the land had been swallowed up by an enormous body of water. Ramti had climbed above the fog and now seemed to be on an uninhabited island surrounded by the sea.

But the minute the sun started its daily round, the

highest and thinnest layer of mist began to evaporate. In the distance Big Stream precipice was a golden red. Then a second, a third, and a fourth ray of sun appeared, and finally it was the turn of Ramti's mountaintop. He shook his fur and turned his back toward the sun. Steam rose around him, and the sun was wonderfully warm. Soon he was completely dry.

From a distance he saw hawks approaching. They looked as if they were falling down from the sky. Ramti looked up at them, and whether he wished it or not, they decided to stop. Screeching and flapping, they flew several turns around him before they were convinced that he wasn't sitting on a delicacy. Then they left him and went gliding over a bog. Drowsily he watched them when they, as on a given signal, suddenly swooped down into the mist. He could no longer see them, but heard them all the more distinctly. Their merry cries in hawk language meant that they had probably found something to eat. They kept coming, and all landed in the same place.

The fog continued to lift. The crowns of some birches became visible, and then a willow and a small rill appeared. Within an hour the valley lay bare, sunny and enticing. And he set off in that direction.

The hawks had settled on the edge of a small bog. Ramti walked up to them—it might be interesting to see what they had found. It turned out to be very rewarding. A dead reindeer was lying there; a big black wolf was circling around it, trying to keep the hawks at bay. They instantly joined forces, but their bargain proved to be of short duration. Ramti exacted an unreasonable price—he wanted all or nothing of the reindeer. And since he was considerably stronger than the hawks and the wolf, it was he alone who enjoyed the breakfast. The wolf took off and the reindeer provided Ramti with a full stomach for several days, during which he never wandered far away. He took afternoon naps or wandered down to the stream to quench his thirst.

One afternoon he had an unexpected visit—a female bear with two cubs following closely in her tracks.

According to custom they sniffed each other. Then they shared the remains of the reindeer. Four bears needed a lot to fill their stomachs, despite the fact that two of them were only cubs. Before they were completely satisfied, they had also cleaned the nearby hill of berries. Then they all lay down to sleep.

A lively time followed. The cubs had the usual facility for getting into mischief. The grouse in the thicket was aroused and chased, also the crane on the bog, and the goose on the tarn, and the plover on the ridge— they all got the same treatment. The cubs even went at the starling in the stream and the wild duck who lived a sheltered life in the reeds. Sometimes the cubs

played tag on the slopes or climbed into trees and wrestled. The most peaceful time was when they were berry picking or sleeping. Only then could the rest of the family settle down to sleep.

Ramti was both amused and worried by his lively family. Like their mother, he tumbled around with them for a while, but never for long. He was too big and slow to keep up with their capers, especially when both cubs came snapping and tugging at him to get his attention. Sometimes he was attacked from both sides. There was always someone biting him in the hind leg or grabbing at his ear. When he used his sternest voice, they quickly moved away, but it was annoying to have to bicker constantly to have a moment's peace— especially when he had just fallen asleep and the cubs descended on him. So he tried to get away from them as often as possible.

The family organized their days into periods of work and rest. They got up at dawn and wandered around trying to find something to eat, after which they took a short nap. Toward evening they got up, and, when it became dark, it was bedtime once more. In that way they made two days and two nights out of twenty-four hours—a clever schedule. At any rate, they had enough time to do what had to be done, and that consisted of finding the best possible berry patches in the valleys around Big Stream.

When the cloudberries withered and became frost-bitten, the bear family moved on to the lingon and crowberry bogs. Morning and evening they stilled their hunger, and the rest of their time was spent resting in the thickets.

These bears represent the whole species for me, and this is the way I last saw them. I have tried to follow Ramti faithfully, and only rarely have I taken excursions into fantasy. When I last saw him, Ramti was standing, legs apart, boldly eating berries from a bush. Next to him the cubs were frolicking around or toddling after their mother. The evening sun was setting on a landscape painted in the colors of autumn. The whole area around the bears was one of harmony. When I left, I fervently wished good luck to these and other bears in our forests and mountains.